Queuing Theory

JOSEPH A. PANICO

Queuing

Theory

A Study of Waiting Lines For

**BUSINESS,
ECONOMICS,
and
SCIENCE**

PRENTICE-HALL, INC., ENGLEWOOD CLIFFS, N.J.

Queuing Theory : A Study of Waiting Lines
for Business, Economics, and Science
BY JOSEPH A. PANICO

© 1969
by PRENTICE-HALL, INC., *Englewood Cliffs, New Jersey*

Printed in the United States of America

Library of Congress Catalog Card No.: *69-15922*
Current Printing (last digit): 10   9   8   7   6   5   4   3   2   1

Prentice-Hall International, Inc., *London*
  Prentice-Hall of Australia, Pty. Ltd., *Sydney*
Prentice-Hall of Canada, Ltd., *Toronto*
  Prentice-Hall of India Private Ltd., *New Delhi*
Prentice-Hall of Japan, Inc., *Tokyo*

Preface

Look at every facet of your daily lives and you will find things moving very fast. Today, for example, our students are entering college with a vastly improved mathematical background. Observe a seventh grade mathematical textbook to gain an appreciation of the revolution that is taking place; consider that these children are working on statements such as:

(a) $\{x \,|\, x \times 6 < 9 \,\wedge\, x > -4\}$

(b) Describe the universe for $(X, Y) = D \times D$ where
$$\{(X, Y) \,|\, Y = -5X^2\}$$

This was unbelievable yesterday but is commonplace today—a growth rate that is truly fantastic.

Experience shows, and many others concur, that the field of quantitative methods, especially with respect to business studies, is also becoming progressively more sophisticated and that these students too are arriving each year with a better mathematical background. It appears, then, that in order to provide books for these students, they be written in a style to complement their new-found ability. As a matter of interest, this year's seventh grade is capable of solving basic systems of linear equations, systems

of linear inequations, and of graphically solving the maximums and mini-
mums of the parameters bound by these inequalities. The eighth grade students are studying permutations, combinations, probabilities, stocastic
processes, measure theory, and other exotic subjects. With knowledge of
what is happening, and the fact that calculus is commonly introduced as a
senior high school subject, we as educators must write college textbooks
that do not presuppose a basic mathematical ignorance with respect to
students. In years of teaching mathematics, I have seen the calculus subjects, formerly considered the fullest extent of one's mathematical exploration, continually introduced at earlier levels. Today, calculus is basically
a freshman study. It may be interesting to note that most mathematical
societies have agreed on the gradual elimination of algebra and trigonometry
as college-level subjects.

Today our colleges and universities are requiring more hours of quantitative subjects for students of business and social science. This accounts
for the popularity of such topics as Econometrics, Sociometrics, Psychome-
trics, Finite Mathematics, Theoretical instead of Descriptive Statistics,
Computer Programming, Calculus for the Social Sciences, and Operations
Research. With these subjects appearing on the curricula, students obviously
have a better quantitative background, otherwise our schools would be in
chaos.

Queuing theory, as a subject, is growing in popularity. It was formerly
restricted to advanced students because of mathematical sophistication.
With today's quantitatively-oriented student it is possible, however, to
explore the rudimentary mathematical queuing problems without encounter-
ing much difficulty. Similarly, the popularity of Monte Carlo procedures
and the availability of computers have allowed the student to examine the
more complex problem through simulation techniques.

This book may be used by a wide set of students studying business,
economics, engineering, and other disciplines of the physical and social
sciences. It is written, however, with primarily business and manufacturing
examples. Most material is presented in order of increasing difficulty, so
that the reader will find various levels of sophistication in specific examples
or chapters. But each topic begins, at an elementary level, thus allowing
for the divergent mathematical backgrounds of students.

As a teacher I have found students more receptive to an educational
approach that centers upon real-world examples. Thus, most examples are
drawn from experiences gained in my consulting work with forty-eight
companies. Some problems have been simplified for teaching purposes, but
others are presented in their entirety for a more comprehensive analysis.
The user will thus find both the simple drill exercise, designed to improve
the set-up and manipulative ability of the reader, and extensive problems
to provide for in-depth study.

This material has been classroom-tested with business students at

Marietta College and Ohio University, engineering students from numerous universities who have enrolled in the evening Operations Research classes, and with students of mathematics; also, specific topics were used in N. M. A. workshops and in an executive training program at Ohio University.

Included in this text is a section devoted to mathematical derivations; they are presented in a separate section but in order of increasing difficulty; business schools may choose not to include this section in their studies. The study of mathematical derivations, however, prior to the study of the chapter "Mathematical Queuing Models," will overcome the problems associated with students accepting formulas on faith alone; if, however, time or level of study will not allow this, then an intuitive approach is given before and with the various examples. Thus, the quantitative chapters may be partitioned by the teacher to suit the background of his students without sacrificing the conceptual aspect of queuing theory.

As a business consultant, I have seen change. Formerly, the only quantitative decision tools came from the Finance or Accounting departments; this is not true today. Other quantitative techniques are contributing to business policy; they center upon: Inventory, Linear Programming, Replacement Models, Game Theory, Markovian Marketing Techniques, and Queuing Theory. These techniques rarely solve a problem per se, but they readily provide the decision-maker with more information, and thus improve the decision-making process.

Queuing Theory: A Study of Waiting Lines was styled as a supplementary textbook. The broad range of examples was selected to provide the reader with knowledge of how to set up and then solve this wide group of problems coming from various business and scientific areas. Included are examples from aircraft, chemical, electronic, food, glass, instrumentation, machining, tobacco, and tool companies. Also included are examples about farm products, hospitals, river dams, and transportation. The example of hospitals is developed from a comprehensive case study of actual data. Other examples use actual data, but it was necessary to modify some problems to better suit the level of sophistication developed in the book. Included also, are solutions found through computer and Markovian analysis. Not only do the examples deal with various businesses and mathematical techniques, but they also deal with the application of queues to other business diciplines. This is why the relationship of queuing theory to marketing problems was developed.

I am particularly indebted to my wife, Mitzi, and to our children Joe, Nina, John, and Paul. My wife edited and typed the manuscript while my children remained quiet—as this was written at home. I am also indebted to my graduate assistants Bob Kramf and, especially, Tom Whipple. Credit is due as well to Professor George Parks of the Wharton School of Finance and Commerce at the University of Pennsylvania, who reviewed the manuscript and made many a helpful suggestion.

Table of Contents

Queuing Theory

1   Introduction

Numerous reasons caused man to colonize—a venture that would have been unsuccessful if he had not learned tolerance, especially that of waiting for others. As the world's population grew so did man's colonies grow into urban communities of various sizes. His life became ordered because he had to rely on the services of others to satisfy his demands. Thus, service from others became a critical function of survival. If man had followed a philosophy of "immediate service on demand," the result would have been an uneconomical utilization of his total effort, and his problems would have been insurmountable. Waiting, therefore, became part of life.

In today's world a waiting line is commonplace and is usually formed by elements, people, machines, or events that "queue up," awaiting service. Some of the classical examples of waiting lines may be found in problems associated with the transportation industry, machine interference, system design, and facilities utilization. In the transportation industry it is frequently found that: airplanes are stacked up over an airport due to traffic congestion and thus are forced to wait in a line for their turn to land; ships and boats also form lines to await docking facilities, harbor pilots, and processing through dams; trucks are queued up waiting for service at shipping docks; and automobiles form queues at bridges, tunnels, and ferries.

In manufacturing economics, one problem is how to assign the correct ratio of man to machine. If a man has responsibilities for too few machines then a considerable portion of his time is nonproductive and some service time is lost for the company. If he is assigned too many machines then machine time may be lost because a man who is servicing one machine is unavailable for work on another. Thus, the total cycle time for one machine is extended because, like others, it must wait for service. This queue of machines, idled because of inadequate servicing, may become extremely costly to a company especially when the cost per machine-hour is considerably larger than the cost per man-hour.

When designing a new system or revamping an old one, engineers and businessmen must be cognizant of the inherent waiting lines. If a machine's or assembly line's feeds and speeds are improperly planned, then additional conveyor belt length or inventorying area would be required to bank the parts prior to the next step in the operation. Supermarkets must plan for adequate check-out systems and servicing systems, for dissatisfaction with waiting lines may restrict buying or cause a loss of customers. Chemical industries, which work constantly with filtration problems, must provide that the particles that are gathered by the filter can be cleared at a rate greater than the particle arrival rate, otherwise the filter will clog and cause the whole system to be idled. Retailers must plan for proper traffic flow patterns throughout the store, and certainly one thing they wish to avoid is oversized waiting lines. Thus, great emphasis is placed on product-, counter-, elevator-, and escalator-layout so as to minimize congestion and queues of people.

Hospital administrators and architects often engage in facilities planning. The hospital of yesteryear has changed considerably, and greater changes are expected in the future. Medical facilities and services are also changing due to new ideas, but primarily because of a change in the types and increasing amounts of service demanded by the input, supplying, population. Governmental laws, changing population and socio-economic characteristics of the incoming patient, the success of birth control, and the conquering of epidemic-type diseases, have created change in hospital planning. Thus, the hospital planners have been forced to re-evaluate their hospital especially with respect to facilities. Waiting lines are commonplace in hospitals and they create emotional hardships for the patient; the patient transfers this frustration to the hospital, and so the administrators must make plans to alleviate the source of the problem. Waiting for food, admittance, surgery, emergency treatment, and laboratory work are part of this over-all frustration, and today hospitals are using mathematical analysis, especially with respect to queues, to help in their planning.

Queuing theory is a mathematical study of waiting lines. Through this study it is possible to isolate such factors as: the average length of the waiting line (how many are in queue); the average time an element, person-machine-event-molecule, must wait in line before service; the expected number of elements in the total system; the expected time an element spends in the total system; probabilities associated with specific events created by the waiting line; and many other characteristics. With this knowledge, it is possible to change the decision-making process, with respect to waiting lines, from a qualitative to a quantitative one, thereby improving the chances of deciding correctly.

Basic queuing theory may be divided into two mathematical studies. One deals with specific type distributions from which mathematical formulas are derived, while the other deals with classical, empirical, or hypothesized distributions which are analyzed through methods of simulation. The former approach is rather restrictive since it requires that the input (supply population) follow a Poisson distribution while the output (servicing) follow an exponential distribution. If these restrictions are satisfied then the problem may be reduced, at least in basic queuing theory, to a process of substitution into the already derived formulae. The latter approach—simulation—allows for a broader study as it is not narrowly bound. Through techniques of simulation, complex models may be abstractly created and studied. This allows the analyst greater flexibility as he may hypothetically change the arrival patterns of the input elements, the service patterns of the output function, or both. With these methods, the analyst may readily study many queuing combinations and thus improve his ability to correctly design a service system.

Queuing theory is important and should be studied because waiting lines disrupt many aspects of life. A basic queuing model has two distinct parts: the waiting line and the service facility. A short line with quick service is required when waiting has a high premium, while a long line with average service may be required when the premium is low. Waiting is usually an economic necessity since most attempts at designing a service system to satisfy demand instantaneously have proven too costly. A line therefore may be loosely interpreted as an inventorying of elements to facilitate economical servicing; yet, in some cases, a waiting line may be that which should be minimized to facilitate economical waiting. This all depends on the input-output relationship and the ratio of their costs. An incorrect design or operating philosophy will magnify all problem areas associated with waiting. Thus, the study of queuing theory must incorporate both the physical and cost characteristics associated with the entire system.

1.1 NATURE AND ORIGIN OF QUEUING THEORY

When demand for a service becomes too great for the servicing capacity, a queue (line) forms. For example, let us consider the situation in which a grocery store cashier can check out twenty-five customers in one hour but there are forty-five customers in that hour waiting to be serviced; since demand exceeds servicing-capacity, a line of customers with their grocery carts forms.

Queuing theory found its first formal application around the beginning of the twentieth century, and there were many scientists who pioneered its advancement.[1] The business and scientific community was receptive to this work since labor costs were rising and management was finding it un-

---

[1] An exceptionally well-written history of Queuing Theory is found in: G.M.F. diRoccaferrera, *Operations Research Models for Business and Industry* (Cincinnati, Ohio: South-Western Publishing Co., 1964, pp. 801–913).

economical to oversupply service. Similarly, this was true in system-design as scientists were being forced to synthesize their processes to speed or expand a system's capabilities.

Queuing theorists found applications for most processes that had random arrivals with limited service, but their efforts were seriously hampered by the complex mathematics required for solution. Thus, the wider such a theory as queuing becomes, the more sophisticated are the mathematical applications. This obviously restricts its usefulness—especially to those who are not specialists in higher mathematics. There is, however, another method which provides a simpler means for problem-solving, and it is called Monte Carlo Analysis. This is a method of simulation which requires less sophistication in terms of mathematical techniques. For this reason, methods of simulation are used widely today, particularly in evaluating queuing problems.

1.2 FIELDS OF APPLICATION

1.21 Application to Business

Queues are found throughout business; consider the following: a food-processing company may have trucks, loaded with perishables, lined up for over twenty-four hours waiting to be unloaded. Not only is spoilage quite possible for the perishables already loaded, but also for those in the fields waiting to be loaded onto the returning trucks. Another queue found frequently in business is that associated with inventory. The queue usually forms while waiting for reorders to come in, but if it is an item easily purchased from others, the problem becomes a queue without a queue, because customers will rarely wait. In manufacturing, queues develop at the toolcrib, the machining areas, and on the assembly line. For example, the operator at the end of the assembly line must wait on the preceding point to pass his output down. In fact, all operations are interdependent: if the beginning machine broke down, work could back up until the whole line was affected. Closely connected to this problem is another that continually plagues both management and labor, for both are concerned with the problem of how many machines to assign one man. This is of vital importance to management when planning new or remodeled plant and production facilities.

Queues are not unique to manufacturing, however, since they are also found in administrative offices. Consider, for example, the paper flow throughout offices, and it will be recognized that queues can bog down this communications system. Consider too the traffic congestion problems with respect to a telephone switchboard. Companies are continually facing the problem of increasing capacity to minimize waiting for a free line. Banks must consider problems related to consumer services since too few bank windows will create large waiting lines. Also associated with queuing theory is the setting aside of new products or projects until there is ample money to invest. The waiting line, here, is the queue of ideas, while service time is the availability of money.

Only a minimum number of queues with business applications have been shown, but these should emphasize the magnitude of the problem. Queues appear everywhere in different types of businesses and service industries. In fact, queues appear in all phases of life.

1.22 Application of Queues to Other Disciplines

Life presents a very large number of queues, some planned and some unexplored. Consider the amount of time wasted, while waiting, in one week, one month, or in a one-year period—no doubt the figure would be startling. In fact, a theory exists for the birth-, life-, and death-process which could lead to the cautious conclusion that life is one big queue, constantly awaiting the next happening. For instance, we wait to shop for, prepare, eat, and digest our food. Even the mental processes must wait until other thoughts are cleared.

Closely related are examples of queues that exist in the physical being. Specific genetic defects can cause inborn errors in metabolism. In one such disorder, a missing principal enzyme causes a substance to accumulate—wait in queue—in the bloodstream, and this eventually damages the brain. Scientists, in studying for the causes and cures of such diseases as cancer and leukemia, have found that the breaking down of the cell process leads to the formation of queues that may disease the system.

In the fields of music and religion, other examples of queues exist. While the comparison may be somewhat vague, mention of some queues peculiar to these fields may be enlightening. In his book "The Mathematical Basic of the Arts," Joseph Schillinger skilfully established the relationships that exist between art and science.[2] He wrote: "If art implies selectivity, skill and organization, ascertainable principles must underly it. Once such principles are discovered and formulated, works of art may be produced by scientific synthesis." If there truly is a mathematical predictability to music and other art-forms, then mathematical formulas could be used in their construction.

[2] Joseph Schillinger, *The Mathematical Basis of the Arts* (New York: Philosophical Library, 1948).

Consider, then, that musical notes in their various combinations may connote fear, love, hate, frustration, gloom, and other emotional responses, and that these arrangements are queued up in a musical score awaiting service by the musician. This servicing of notes can most assuredly cause problems, as attested by many unwilling listeners to beginning trumpet players. From a more technical position, notes often form waiting lines (interference) when their harmonic waves, of different frequencies, act simultaneously for the production of a new sequence.

In the Roman Catholic Church priests must plan for large queues at the altar during specific periods of the year, especially at Easter and Christmas, because of unusually large numbers of parishioners receiving communion at these times. They also must plan for a heavier demand during the midmorning masses than during earlier services.

Thus it appears that queuing theory finds application in most areas, demonstrating the divergent nature of the problem. The theory can be or has been applied to any of the following areas: inventories; post office backlog; large backlog in our court systems; catalysts in a chemical reaction; filtration processes; gas molecules going through a hole; semiconductor noise; hospitals and the demand for medical care; nervous reactions, and such psychological stress and strain as neurosis. Then there are the many services that modern man demands—barbers, shops of all sorts, utilities, and mass transporation. Queues were shown to develop in production lines, inspection lines, conveyor belts, and communications. Finally, one of the most important uses is to establish the correct man-machine ratio to thus minimize machine interference.

Although the list is probably endless and examples could be found in all our disciplines, it should be pointed out that not all sizable queues are necessarily undesirable. There is an air of anticipation and excitement in waiting for certain events such as plays, trips, exhibitions, and athletic events. Queues were a common sight during the exhibition of the Pietà at the World Fair of 1964–65. A queue in front of the theater is also a good omen for the theater-owner—it means a full house and adds the special attraction of free advertisement to any passerby.

1.3 QUEUING CHARACTERISTICS AND TERMINOLOGY

A queue forms when demand for service is greater than servicing capacity. These demands emanate from finite or infinite sources. A finite source usually implies a small countable set such as twenty machines with twenty operators who must at random intervals go to a tool crib for replacement tooling. Here, when one operator goes from his machine for service, the probability of another operator's leaving for service is reduced as these departures are dependent events. An infinite source requires a large set to provide the input to the system. This implies an unlimited supply of people or things that will demand service. In such cases, each event is considered as independent of another. In actual practice, an infinite approach is often used when the source comes from a large finite population. This is permissible because a large finite source usually yields a finite approximation of an infinite situation. An example of such an infinite approach would be customers waiting to be checked out of a grocery supermarket. A grocery store may easily have 10,000 to 15,000 customers per week with a great number of these engaged in cross-shopping. The set of customers of one week, therefore, may be substantially different from that of another.

1.31 Dependency-Independency Relationships

As an example of dependency and independency, consider an area that has twelve machine operators and one drinking fountain. Many random observations of this area will yield empirical probabilities for one, two, three, four, . . . twelve operators getting a drink. The probability of one operator's being absent is higher than the probability of two; two greater than three; eleven greater than twelve. It may then be concluded that finding one operator at the fountain reduces the probability of another's arriving during the same interval if the Pr (one arrival) $> Pr$ (two arrivals)$/Pr$ (one arrival).[3] Note:

$$Pr \text{ (one arrival)} > \frac{Pr \text{ (two arrivals)}}{Pr \text{ (one arrival)}}$$

For another example, consider an urn that has ten black balls and fifteen white balls. If one ball is drawn at random there is a probability $\frac{10}{25}$ that it is black. If the ball is not replaced the probability of drawing another black is $\frac{9}{24}$. By the multiplication principle, the probability of drawing two black balls when the first is not replaced is $(\frac{10}{25})(\frac{9}{24})$. If the first ball were replaced, then the second draw or subsequent draws would always originate from an equivalent set. The probability of drawing a black on the first draw would equal $\frac{10}{25}$. If the ball is replaced, the probability of drawing a black ball on the second draw is also $\frac{10}{25}$. The probability of drawing two black balls in sequence under these conditions is $(\frac{10}{25})(\frac{10}{25})$. This leads, with caution, to a

---

[3] Pr (black) and P (black) are read: The probability of black. Pr and P are used synonymously throughout this book as meaning probabilities.

conclusion: two events are independent when Pr (one black) $= Pr$ (two black) $/Pr$ (one black), and they are dependent when the Pr (one black) $> Pr$ (two black)$/Pr$ (one black). Here, in the dependency situation, it was shown that one draw of black reduced the probability of another draw of black. If the urn contained 25,000 balls mixed in the same proportion, it may be seen that the difference between a dependent and an independent probability is extremely small. Dependent probabilities, in this example, for two successive draws would be $(\frac{10,000}{25,000})(\frac{9999}{24,999})$. Comparing this to the previous example will show that $(\frac{10,000}{25,000})(\frac{9999}{24,999}) > (\frac{10}{25})(\frac{9}{24})$. In many cases, therefore, when the set is large (for example, two hundred instead of twelve operators) it is permissible to use formulas for infinite queues instead of finite queues. However, caution should be used.

In a problem involving an infinite source, the probabilities are independent because an observation of one event will not reduce the probabilities of another similar event, when the second event is considered individually. The set always maintains its original infinite size. For an example of the possibilities originating from an infinite source, consider Flying Saucer enthusiasts who have claimed sightings in a particular area. If the reports show 201 sightings, how many Flying Saucers were not observed? Here, the size of the set, or number of trials, is unknown. Each event, therefore, should be considered independent. In dealing with such situations, statisticians have found the Poisson distribution quite applicable, and formulas for queues originating from an infinite source are derived using this approach.

1.32 Classification of Queues

Most service systems are designed so that average servicing capacity is greater than average arrivals for service. But even with this excess capacity to clear, a line will still form. If these arrivals were equally spaced or paced, then the flow rate could be guaranteed for any time period. For example: if a machine dropped a finished part on a conveyor every five seconds, then the arrival rate would be constant and easily predictable. Thus with this paced input a line would not form, since the servicing system was designed with excess clearing capacity.

When arrivals are not equally spaced or paced, there will be time intervals where the number of arrivals is less than, equal to, or greater than, servicing capacity. For example: a small branch bank averages fifteen savings-account customers per hour. If a teller can service an average of twenty per hour, then one bank window should be sufficient; but large lines form because there are specific time intervals where arrivals exceed servicing capacity. In the early morning hours, a bank window will not have demands for service from fifteen customers, but at noon time it will usually have demands in excess of servicing capacity. Thus, service rates greater than arrival rates will prevent the formation of lines, since the unused servicing capacity from the morning hours cannot be stored for future use during times of heavier demands.

A system usually begins with one serving station. As demand grows heavier or the nature of the service changes, then additional capacity must be provided. Thus, a servicing system may take on a number of basic forms: One Line–One Server, One Line–Multiple Server, and Station-to-Station Models. There are other combinations which are more complex, but even the elementary forms may become complex models when the servicing discipline changes. The examples previously described were based on a first come–first served discipline. But if customers or elements with priorities received immediate service regardless of line size, then even these elementary models would be complicated.

Queues were previously classified as developing from a finite or infinite source. They may also be classified according to the following specific characteristics:

One Line–One Server

Boats and barges waiting to be processed through one river dam lock. In this example, the waiting boats, served on a first come–first served basis, represent the line; the one lock used for raising or lowering the boats represents the one server situation. See Fig. 1.1.

Figure 1.1

One servicing lock

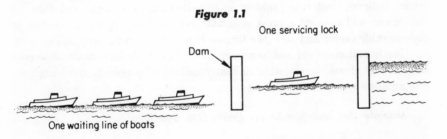

One waiting line of boats

Discipline: Boats serviced on a first come — first served basis

One Line–Multiple Server

A barber shop with four chairs operating on a first come–first served basis (NO customer preference allowed, which certainly is a hypothetical case). See Fig. 1.2.

Figure 1.2

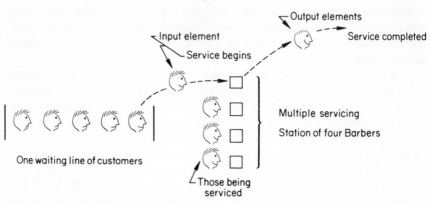

Discipline: Customers serviced on first come – first served basis

Multiple Line–Multiple Server (Without Line Switching)

An Army private is told he must get his immunization shots for overseas duty. To hasten this lengthy process, all the men of the regiment are processed alphabetically. A–C in line one, D–F in line two, G–J in line three . . . Y–Z in lines eight and nine. He must be serviced by his own line, regardless of the other lines' speed or size, for his records are kept there, and this is the Army's way (the latter consideration being the more significant). If the reader believes that this problem is hypothetical, it is suggested that an enlistment will provide a most unusual first-hand experience of queues of unbelievable origin and size (the former being more prevalent).

Mathematicians do not consider this a multiple-line, multiple-server situation. It should be classified as many individual problems involving one-line and one-server.

Multiple Line–Multiple Server (With Line Switching)

There are three elevators in a department store. Customers group around each elevator hoping to be moved to their destination in the shortest time. If elevator number two arrives first, some members on the edge of groups one and three will switch to two hoping that this will help move them faster.

Station to Station

In the event of community immunization during a catastrophe, vaccine is administered in small communities on a first come–first served basis. Oral

Polio Vaccine may be used as an example. A family group goes to the check-in station, waits in line for processing, and then proceeds through this station to another for service. In this case, the family which forms the first line also forms the second. This is a case of random arrival with random service (size of family varies) at the first station followed by random arrival with random service at the second station.

There are many variations of this dependency relationship. For example, constant service in the first station usually results in a constant arrival at the second.[4]

Other classifications

Queues may be further classified by special situations, and these are obviously many. Some frequently encountered are: priorities, customer preference, and line-balking. The mathematics required for a special situation is usually complex but may find an easier solution through methods of simulation.

1.33 Additional Queue Combinations

Queues were previously differentiated by describing the relationship that exists when one or more lines demand service from one or more servicing

[4] Dependency relationships are often found in business. In such a relationship one event precedes another with the second being generally dependent on the first. Consider one operator who runs two machines with the second being dependent on the first. If the first had few interruptions while the second had many, a large queue would form at the second. Another dependency relationship, also designated as tandem processing, may be found in the assembly departments where all component parts converge on a line for final processing. An assembly line requires sequential operations, so a dependency relationship clearly exists between stations on the line as one operation is dependent on its predecessor. Any delay in the first could cause a delay in the second; also, any change of pace from either station causes a change in the queue size. Many other dependency situations exist in business, some being: annunciation systems in chemical companies; circuitry in an electronically controlled system that utilizes time-delay relays or modules to store signals until the next component, or station, is ready to accept it; departures from a grocery supermarket where first the customer is in line, the bill totaled, and groceries are carried out. This is extremely important to a grocer, as too long a line at the cash register annoys the customer and also too long a wait for a carryout boy can similarly result in customer dissatisfaction. If the system is over-designed there will be too many cashiers and carry outs; then every sale could be unprofitable. Vladimir Nabokov described in his book *Bend Sinister*[5] a unique series of station to station queues created by the new laws of transportation imposed by the government. One example of these new laws: three or more people must wish to depart the bus; otherwise it would not stop. Station-to-station queues are generally complex, especially when they originate in a real world setting, and mathematicians have found that these are better solved through methods of simulation.

[5] Vladimir Nabokov, *Bend Sinister* (New York: Time Incorporated Time Reading Program, 1964).

stations. These may be further refined by letting the arrivals or service be either random or constant. The possibilities that now exist are:

Constant Arrivals–Constant Service
Random Arrivals–Constant Service
Constant Arrivals–Random Service
Random Arrivals–Random Service

The magnitude of the queuing problem becomes apparent because these new refinements considerably increase the number of queue combinations.

Some examples of these are:

Constant Arrival and Random Service

An automated furnace supplies a heated shovel blank to an operator every half minute. The operator requires an average of three-eighths of a minute to process the heated part. He must complete his task within a half minute since processing of the next blank cannot be delayed. If he stops the furnace, the blanks will become too hot and be unusable. If the furnace is not stopped, any processing delay will force the operator to discard the cooled piece. The company wants to have this process as synchronized as possible to reduce labor costs and minimize the cost of reheating unused blanks. The union wants one shovel blank supplied every three-fourths of a minute because unprocessed blanks represent a loss in incentive opportunity; the union then files a grievance.

Random Arrivals and Constant Service

Queues coming from an infinite source form in front of a booth selling tickets for a carnival ride. The service at the booth is randomized depending on the number of tickets purchased and the requirements for change. Once the tickets are purchased, the customers proceed to the ride and generally arrive there in the random manner dictated by the previous station, the ticket booth. Once all customers are secured in their seats, the ride begins and, after five revolutions, is abruptly ended. This is a station-to-station queue, the first being random-random and the second, with tongue in cheek, being random-constant.

A prime example of an arrival from an infinite population with absolutely constant service may be found when examining the Taxi Dance Emporiums of the 1920's–40's. Here is found a classical example of service termination irrespective of customer demands, since the service was paced by a band or record player, and the young ladies were extremely adept at disposing of patrons of the art.

1.4 DISCUSSION AND REVIEW QUESTIONS

1. Find three additional queues as applied to areas other than business and engineering. Briefly describe how an ability to predict the queue would greatly minimize the problem.

2. Give an example of a: (a) One Line–One Server Queue coming from an infinite population when the service is not on a first come–first served basis; (b) Station-to-Station Queue with priorities in the second station; (c) Multiple Line–Multiple Server Queue (with line switching) in a marketing situation where the line-size does not have detrimental effects on business.

3. When a manager gets a mathematical solution to a waiting line problem from his Operations Research Group, should he accept it completely or modify it using his own intuition?

4. Mathematics is a way of thinking. Queuing theory must therefore be classified as a way of thinking. Comment.

5. How would you rule, as an arbitrator, in the Shovel Blank Problem? See Sec. 1.33.

6. A manager of a large discount store determined that during the week he will need only four check-out stations as against the eight normally required on weekends. In August the number of customers on Mondays, Tuesdays, and Wednesdays was 10,000, and sales on these days amounted to $30,000. On Thursdays, Fridays, and Saturdays there were 20,000 customers and $100,000 worth of sales. Subjectively determine whether his reasoning is correct.

7. A challenging method of determining your intuitive understanding of queuing theory is to draw analogical characteristics of the following ideas with business.

   (a) Harry, a scientist engaged in pure research, was riding a bicycle and came to a corner. While waiting for the traffic to clear he tried balancing himself, only to find that it was impossible; yet when he was moving fast or slow, balance presented no problem. He immediately concluded that this phenomenon had business implications. He continued to ponder this problem and further concluded that if the waiting time were exceedingly long he might die before ever gaining equilibrium through momentum.

   (b) Pierre Simon, Marquis De Laplace, questioned in his book "A Philosophical Essay on Probabilities"[6] the authenticity of history. He hypothe-

---

[6] Pierre Simon, Marquis De Laplace, *A Philosophical Essay on Probabilities*, (New York: Dover Publications, Inc., 1951, pp. 13–19).

sized that if the first historical writings were approximately ninety percent accurate, the second writings which used these and others for reference would similarly be approximately ninety percent accurate; it may then be easily seen that accuracy through time is diminishing—eventually approaching zero. He believed that historians did not give enough attention to this "degradation of events," and that many historical facts considered absolute would falter somewhat when tested this way. From this general idea he challenged certain decisions for the future because they used past events for documentation that to him were not admissible. If Laplace is right, then queuing theory takes on added importance. Consider forecasting and the wait for feedback information. What about line size and the near past being more reliable than a more distant past? Experience may be considered as a line of events; could this line hold back new, radically different ideas? Can one rely on publications that may come solely from library research? If this idea were depicted, historical events could be the line waiting for service by statisticians, economists, scientists, and others.

Write a summary of your thoughts on sections (a) and (b) to determine the validity of decision-making with these thoughts in mind.

2   Machine Interference:

2.1 MACHINE INTERFERENCE DEFINED

When one operator is assigned two machines there is a possibility—sometimes very small, but depending on the ratio of man time to machine time—that one machine will require his services while he is engaged in work on the other. If the number of machines is increased, the probability of one interfering with the normal cycle of another is similarly increased. Any variation of the number of machines or the ratio of man time to machine time will affect the degree of interference. This situation, called "Machine Interference," has been responsible for a great quantity of managerial problems such as increased union activities, generally grievances, misplanned facilities, inefficient operations, poor machine utilization, improper crew sizes, and other situations extremely troublesome to the efficient operation of an enterprise.

As man's technical knowledge increases, the more mechanized his industries become. This generally results in a greater number of machines being

A First Look at Queuing Theory

assigned to the individual or crew. Historically man has attempted to reduce the ratio of his work time (hand time) to machine-running time. This reduced ratio is desirable because it permits management to increase the machine assignment or reduce the crew size to yield a greater productivity per man-hour. As in most systems there are economical levels for operations, which means machine assignments cannot become infinite. This problem, the correct assignment of man to machine, has excited the imaginations of many competent mathematicians who have remarkably approached reality through their exploration of this probabilistic model. Their successes are numerous and research is continuing, but often these formulas only approximate the real situation. The prevalent mathematical techniques used in solving machine interference problems are binomial, normal, and exponential. Attempts at a binomial and stochastic explanation of machine interference are limited; yet this explanation is useful when dealing with small machine assignments, and is easily understood by the nonmathematician when presented in elementary form. The nonquantitative manager or union official is more receptive to this simplified approach which may justify overlooking the slight error in the binomial model of not accounting for cumulative interference. Mathematicians have in recent years found ways to correct this error, to some extent broadening use of this approach. The other systems, normal and exponential, which are moderately complex, have the advantage of accuracy but lack simplicity. Many mathematicians show their analysis graphically, and this is a commendable step toward simplification. The problem, however, is to convince the machine operator that he should assume responsibility for six instead of four machines. Armed with a grievance or the humanistic philosophy, a worker may very well show the futility of mathematically tracking machine interference to a high degree of accuracy.

Why should so much emphasis be placed on machine interference? One answer is that when designing a new facility it is imperative that engineers have mathematical methods available for exploring the effects of machine interference vis-à-vis equipment utilization. It is also important that some method be available to create the man-to-machine work situation abstractly. If this technique were not available the probability is strong that original crew-to-machine assignments would have greater inaccuracies. When too few machines are originally assigned, then management will experience extreme difficulty in moving up to the correct point. Similarly, an attempt to start with a higher machine-to-man ratio could be equally disastrous because it would foster distrust within the laboring group and first-line managers who through actual operation might find the work situation quite different from that which was advocated. This situation magnifies when incentives are involved because a misassignment may reduce the operator's incentive opportunity. In the past it was not unusual to have teams of time-study men engaged in eight-hour time studies to determine the effect of interferences, only to find that the data were not representative. Work-sampling techniques helped to alleviate the cost and shortcomings of the actual study, but once more cost and representation presented some limitations. Formulas as a somewhat accurate guide provide management with a measurement device to begin analysis.

One of the most important uses of the mathematical approach is to focus attention on the magnitude of the problem. Examples of managerial unawareness are numerous. The following example, while abbreviated, is a moderately complex problem from a real-world situation.

2.2 A CASE HISTORY OF MACHINE INTERFERENCE WITHIN A CHEMICAL INDUSTRY

The majority of chemical companies are heavily automated. They are a continuous-type processing industry that maintain tight controls over their products. Many types of sophisticated equipment are used to provide the operators an instantaneous feedback with respect to tolerances, viscosities, turbulence, flow rates, and other control-critical areas. Instrumentation is a major factor with the industry as it provides an immediate audit of the total system.

Chemical companies invest heavily in special-purpose equipment and generally require considerable acreage for their facilities. They occupy a unique position as their ratio of sales per man-hour usually exceeds that of other industries. This favorable position is an outgrowth of automation.

A product is considered for continual processing when demand, marketability, and technological competition warrant it; many years may pass before this point is reached. A chronological series of events for developing a product usually involves research, limited production, and continuous processing respectively ordered. Achieving this final position is a major accomplishment, and few products survive this test.

Ideas for new products originate in many areas with research and sales departments being the major contributors. Probabilities for success of a new idea are weak, but those which satisfy the constraints imposed by the various departments are considered for limited production. The limitations are caused by many factors. Some are: price of a new product, limited original market, inability to maintain product uniformity, and others. With these as problem areas, a chemical company may wisely choose to manufacture this product on a pilot-limited production-basis until the majority of problems are resolved. To embark immediately on a continuous production basis would be extremely dangerous, with one of the principal contributors of risk being the high facilities cost.

One area commonly found in chemical industries is a batch-processing area. This is a general-purpose area with capabilities to run many products. Orders may be long- or short-run depending on customer demands, forecasting, and inventory levels. Scheduling takes on added importance as the incompatibility of certain chemicals may create unfavorable reactions which will require that the reactor be cleaned when changing to a new product. This is an exceptionally costly process, and one of the scheduling functions is to order a sequence of compatible products whenever possible so as to reduce the conversion time. Priority given to specific orders also affects the scheduling process and has an equally disturbing influence on the operational division.

Chemical companies use many systems for measuring the performance of their operational areas. Equipment utilization is one of these. Their analysis, however, often overlooks the effects of machine interference; yet this factor could be substantially reducing their equipment utilization.

Management may assign one crew more than one reactor. Their work routine requires that they load and unload each reactor whenever the process is completed. Frequency studies show that the external and internal crew work plus reaction times is randomly distributed.

In the following case all data are changed and considerably simplified for presentation purposes since batch-processing problems may require special consideration regardless of the mathematical approach because of long cycle times. The purpose of this case therefore is to introduce a binomial approach without regard to specialized cases. Consider the following situation:

2.21 Case History—Interference in the Batch-Processing Department

The supervisor of a batch-processing department has received a production schedule calling for the manufacture of 50,000 pounds of product #221. This product is easy to run, and cycle times are readily predictable. Some rough calculations, based on past historical data, indicate that an average of three hours is required for the crew to service one reactor—load, drum, and clean—and that average reaction time is six hours. This means that the average total cycle time per batch approximates nine hours. The supervisor has available two, three, or four reactors to get this production out on schedule, but he is operating on a very close cost. If his decisions were wrong, the company could lose money on this order. He gathers all available information and confers with both his supervisors and his subordinates. His total labor cost per hour, which includes operators and fringes, is about $25, while the reactor has a $65 per hour cost.

The ensuing discussions yield the following opinions. The crew: "We cannot economically service more than two reactors." The supervisor: "I believe that three reactors can be worked by our crew and that this will help us to meet our delivery date." The management: "I should think that our most economical set-up would be four reactors, as this would utilize all of our equipment and keep the crew completely busy."

Figure 2.1 shows a bar chart of one reactor's average total cycle time. This type of chart is frequently used for production control purposes.

Figure 2.1

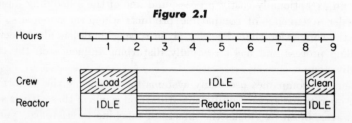

* Crew Utilization = $(TDT)/(TCT) = \frac{3}{9} = 33.3\%$ (Crew occupies 33.3% of total cycle) and Reactor Utilization = $TRT/TCT = \frac{6}{9} = 66.7\%$ (Reactor used 66.7% of total cycle) where: TDT = Total Down Time = Reactor down for service by crew; TCT = Total Cycle Time, TRT = Total Reaction (Machine) Time, TMT = Total Machine Time.

Remember that interference is included in the down time figures.

Figure 2.2

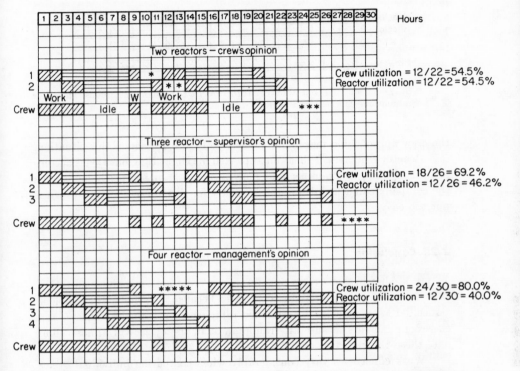

* Reactor is delayed from start of new cycle because loading cannot be partially undertaken as unfavorable reaction will begin; also the unloading (drumming) operation must commence soon after reaction, otherwise the product will lose some of its characteristics.

** Crew cannot service both reactors simultaneously. Crew is working on #1, therefore #2 must wait.

*** Notice that crew utilization has improved compared with one reactor. Evaluate the new utilization by considering only one reactor and then compare with how much the crew has been utilized during one reactor time. The cycle time for one reactor has been extended to eleven minutes because another reactor was added, but crew utilization has improved.

**** Crew efficiency is improving but reactor utilization is decreasing. Management must determine what course to follow—better crew utilization or better reactor utilization.

***** Reactor #1 is waiting because crew must service reactors #1, #2, #3, and #4 in that order.

Figure 2.2 shows bar charts of all three opinions. Remember all data were gathered from historical records and frequency studies which, in this case, means that interference is included as part of the crew work time.

After reviewing these charts, the supervisor was confused as to which system would return the most profit. Upon re-evaluation of the three reactor charts, he found that a slight change in working procedure created a situation in which the reactors became approximately sixty-seven percent utilized with

Figure 2.3

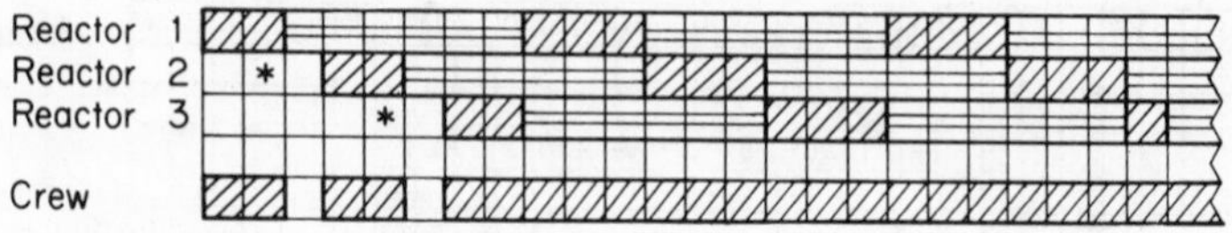

* Staggered starting time allows all future cycles to become continuous. The other combinations can be similarly improved with staggering.

the crew approaching maximum efficiency. Figure 2.3 shows this situation.

Reactor- and crew-utilization approach maximization, but this is accomplished by idling the number four reactor at a cost of $65 per hour—unless the company can schedule another product for this unused facility, which is not too easy.

2.22 Conclusion

It is shown that staggering improves crew and machine utilization. This, however, only represents ideal cases because it excludes the problems associated with machine interference. Staggering is valueless except as a classroom exercise because any randomness in the cycle will almost eliminate these theoretical benefits.

Work efficiencies vary considerably when comparing individual cycles. This has the effect of either extending or contracting the external–internal work times. There are many reasons for this changing efficiency, with one major contributor being the cumulative effect of fatigue. Analysts have shown that efficiency changes by the hour, day, week, and shift. These inconsistencies, coupled with a varying reaction time, complicate any mathematical solution. It is unusual to find a completely predictable total cycle time since there are many factors such as machine breakdown, preventive maintenance, morale, accidents, sickness, featherbedding when expecting a layoff, and others that affect any analysis. The mathematical model, therefore, is usually developed along probabilistic lines in order to predict the expected situation.

Many factors other than machine and crew utilization will influence the final decision when considering the preferred solution in the real-life model. If a production schedule must be met to satisfy customers' demands then some inefficient machine or crew groupings will be tolerated. Cost is another factor for consideration as are inventory levels, sales forecasts, and current industry outlook. These problems most assuredly complicate the decision-making process and certainly reduce the possibilities of finding a perfect solution.

This example, which encompasses all the previously-described problem areas, actually improved management decision-making because it brought out the magnitude of machine interference and its effect on a particular department. Even though the model was subject to some error it was easily presented and readily understood. It clearly pointed out the effect of machine interference; thus the associated problems such as scheduling, delivery, and equipment utilization were improved. The magnitude of this problem helped plant-level management justify to the executive group a need for silo storage of chemicals. This new equipment reduced crew work time substantially and resulted in an improved equipment utilization.

2.3 TYPES OF SERVICING

2.31 Synchronous Servicing

In the analysis of machine interference it is quite common to characterize the man-to-machine relationship as synchronous, random, or mixed. Synchronous servicing implies that operator times and machine times are completely predictable for each cycle since they do not vary from one trial to another. A synchronous situation exists when all the operator time is used per cycle with no delay to any machine. A perfect situation would result if all available operator time were divided equally among machines with identical machine running time. The number of machines possible for an operator or crew to service would be determined by dividing operator time per machine into the total cycle time.

$N =$ Use smallest whole number to establish the number of machines possible for one operator or crew to service $\dfrac{TCT}{TWT}$

The chemical company example, if times were constant instead of random, would indicate that:

$$N = \frac{TCT}{TWT} = \frac{9}{3} = 3 \quad \text{machines (reactors)}$$

This calls for uninterrupted in-step servicing, which obviously is an ideal case as both man and machine theoretically lose no part of their cycle after start-up because of another machine. Any assignment greater than N would require one machine to wait for another, introducing interference. If the value of N were $2\frac{3}{4}$ instead of 3.0 then theoretically only two machines should be required, and this would introduce a substantial slack in the system; but if this analysis considered an incentive rather than a normal pace, then three machines could be required. In reality even the perfect situation develops interference, and mathematicians have developed formulas for predicting its relationship to the total cycle.

2.32 Random Servicing

Random servicing problems cannot be easily graphed because the situation depicted can only be a special representation of the numerous possibilities. In the example of the chemical company it was originally established that crew and reactor times were based on averages. These graphs, as shown in the original example, symbolize a perfect situation where all reactors and crews strike their averages. This is indeed a rare situation. When interference is mathematically determined and included as part of the graph, it will give a pictorial representation of the expected situation provided that a sufficient number of trials have occurred.[1]

2.33 Mixed Servicing

A mixed situation exists when one segment of the cycle is constant and the other random. Consider one operator who has responsibility for two semi-automatic machines: his work time is random, while machine time is constant. If the example of the chemical company were a mixed servicing problem, it would require that the crew times of load and unload be variable with the reaction time constant.

2.4 MATHEMATICAL APPROACHES

The mathematical solutions to machine interference may be generally classified as algebraic and probabilistic. The algebraic solutions imply constant times; this is extremely rare because a portion of the cycle is controlled by an operator whose work time varies from one cycle to another. The other

---

[1] Averages come from a frequency distribution; thus, these graphs only show what may be expected. If each total cycle time were classified as above average, normal, or below average, then there would be 3^2, 3^3, 3^4, combinations for two, three, and four reactors respectively. There are, however, an infinitesimal number of combinations as each category, in itself, could be infinitely partitioned. Thus each combination of events will yield above-or-below-normal interference, with the average of these being equal to the expected interference. Individual sets of conditions yield varying amounts of interference which, in turn, may affect the combination of events that follow. This condition results in dependency of one set of events on another, which could be loosely interpreted as interference creating interference.

approach, which uses probabilities, deals with completely random or partially random total cycles, with the latter best typifying the real-world setting.

2.41 Algebraic Analysis: Constant Time Situation

Given:

$$TET_1 \quad \text{(External Hand Time)} = 3 \text{ min}$$
$$TIT_1 \quad \text{(Internal Hand Time)} = 2 \text{ min}$$
$$TWT_1 = TET + TIT \quad \text{(Total Work Time)} = 5 \text{ min}$$
$$TMT_1 = \text{(Machine Time)} = 11 \text{ min}$$
$$TCT_1 = \text{(External Hand Time + Machine Time)}$$
$$= 14 \text{ min}$$
$$N = \text{Number of Machines}$$
$$MC = \text{(Machine Cost)} = \$25/\text{hr} = \$25/60$$
$$= \$.417 \text{ per min}$$
$$LC = \text{(Labor Cost)} = \$5/\text{hr} = \$5/60$$
$$= \$.083 \text{ per min}$$
$$N \leq \frac{TCT}{TWT} = \frac{14}{15} = 2.8$$
$$N = 2 \quad \text{(Eight-tenths machine cannot be assigned)}$$

If $N = 3$, interference will be introduced into the system as the process becomes completely controlled by the operator.

Figure 2.4 illustrates the various constant time situations. The first two illustrate a situation in which the cycle is partially controlled by the machine, while the third shows a situation completely controlled by the operator.

In the first illustration of one operator and one machine: Machine #1 is considered operational for the complete Total Cycle (TCT) even though idle during TET_1. Operator is also paid for idle time of $TMT_1 - TIT_1$.

$$\text{COST} = TCT(MC) + TCT(LC) = 14(\tfrac{25}{60}) + 14(\tfrac{5}{60}) = \$7.00$$

The second illustration of one operator running two machines shows that:

Cost per machine remains $TCT(MC)$, while labor cost is divided between two machines.

$$\text{COST} = \frac{N(TCT)(MC) + TCT(LC)}{N} = \frac{2(14)(\tfrac{25}{60})}{2} + \frac{14(\tfrac{5}{60})}{2} = \$6.42$$

where

$$\text{Machine Cost} = TCT(MC) \quad \text{and} \quad \text{Operator Cost} = \frac{TCT(LC)}{N}$$

When the work assignment is again increased, one operator is responsible for three machines. Notice that the machine cost for the system will remain constant until $N(TWT_1) > TCT$. When this occurs, interference has been introduced into the system since the machine must wait for the

Figure 2.4

Man – Machine Charts   (Constant Times – Synchronous Servicing)

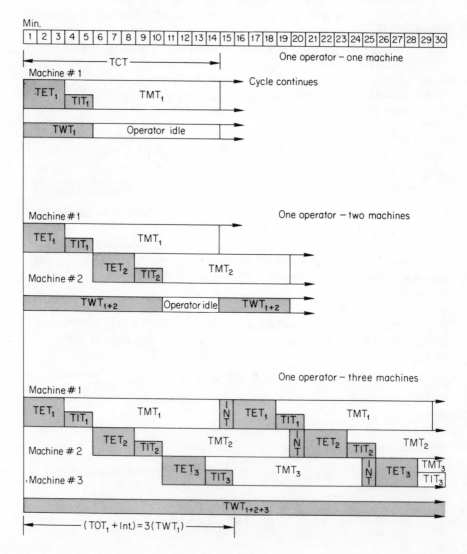

operator. The TCT is unrestricted by the machine. Interference for this situation is divided equally among the machines, which happens only in those cases involving identical operations.

$$\text{COST} = \frac{N(TWT_1)(LC) + N[N(TWT_1)(MC)]}{N}$$

$$= \frac{(15)(\frac{5}{60}) + (3)(15)(\frac{25}{60})}{3} = \$6.67$$

Interference has increased the machine cost in the third case by one minute, which at \$25/hr is equivalent to \$.42 per cycle. Thus the impact of interference can be seen in this exceptionally simplified model. Remember that hand time has been reduced, acccounting for the total cost of \$6.67.

2.42 Probabilistic Analysis: Random Times (Binomial solution with interference included in the down time)

This leaves for solution the situation involving completely random and partially random cycles. These are best handled through the use of probabilities. In the first solution, attention will be given the completely randomized situation as previously described in the example of the chemical

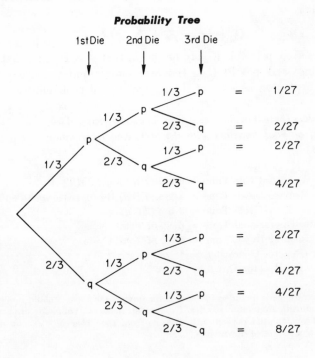

Probability Tree

company. One method frequently used is a stochastic process of independent trials which requires the use of probabilities. A traditional example is the diagram showing one throw of three dice when a two or a five is desired.

$$Pr \text{ (of a two or five)} = Pr\,(2 \vee 5)$$

thus

$$p = \text{successful event} = Pr(2 \vee 5) = \tfrac{2}{6} = \tfrac{1}{3}$$

$$q = \text{failure} \qquad\quad = 1 - p = Pq(2 \vee 5) = \tfrac{4}{6} = \tfrac{2}{3}$$

All eight possibilities have been covered with respect to order as $ppp = \frac{1}{27}$, $pqp = \frac{2}{27}$, $qpp = \frac{2}{27}$, $pqq = \frac{4}{27}$ and $qqq = \frac{8}{27}$, etc. In this example, however, combinations instead of permutations are desired. Thus, single events pqp, ppq, and qpp are considered similar, thereby leaving the following possibilities:

Three	p's $= ppp$	$= \tfrac{1}{27}$	(all 2's or 5's)
Two	p's $= ppq,\ pqp,\ qpp = \tfrac{2}{27} + \tfrac{2}{27} + \tfrac{2}{27} = \tfrac{6}{27}$		(two 2's or 5's)
One	$p\ \ = pqq,\ qpq,\ qqp = 3(\tfrac{4}{27})$	$= \tfrac{12}{27}$	(one 2 or 5)
Zero	p's $= qqq$	$= \tfrac{8}{27}$	(zero 2's or 5's)

These could also have been predicted through the binomial expansion of $(p + q)^n$, which provides probabilistic values for all combinations. In this example it is

$$(\tfrac{1}{3} + \tfrac{2}{3})^3 = \tfrac{1}{27} + \tfrac{6}{27} + \tfrac{12}{27} + \tfrac{8}{27}$$

Using this same principle it may be shown that $p = \text{Pr}$ (i.e., that a reactor is operating) and $q = \text{Pr}$ (i.e., that a reactor requires service) follow an identical expansion because of the equivalence of probabilities.

Consider These Possibilities: One Crew Servicing Two, Three, or Four Reactors with the Following Information Given:

$$\text{Reactor Cycle Time} = 6 \text{ hrs } (TRT) \text{ or } (TMT)$$
$$\text{Reactor Down Time} = 3 \text{ hrs } (TDT) \text{ Interference included}[2]$$
$$\text{Total Cycle Time} = 9 \text{ hrs } (TCT)$$
$$\text{Reactor Operational Time} = 67\% \text{ of Total Cycle}$$
$$\text{Reactor Down Time} = 33\% \text{ of Total Cycle}$$
$$\text{Pr (Reactor Operating)} = \tfrac{2}{3}$$
$$\text{Pr (Reactor Down)} = \tfrac{1}{3}$$

[2] Interference is included in the reactor down time since it could not be recorded separately during frequency studies. To find an accurate value for crew work time, subtract the calculated percent interference from the observed percent down time. Crew time is a subset of down time.

CALCULATING MACHINE INTERFERENCE FOR TWO REACTORS

Binomial Probability Distribution $= (p + q)^n = (\frac{2}{3} + \frac{1}{3})^2$

1st Term = Zero Down, Two Operating[3] $= b(2; 2, \frac{2}{3}) = \frac{4}{9}$
2nd Term = One Down, One Operating $= b(1; 2, \frac{2}{3}) = \frac{4}{9}$
3rd Term = Two Down, Zero Operating $= b(0; 2, \frac{2}{3}) = \frac{1}{9}$

Probability Tree

1st Reactor	2nd Reactor	Path Weight	Description
	Operating	4/9	Zero reactors down
Operating	Down	2/9	One reactor down
	Operating	2/9	One reactor down
Down	Down	1/9	Two reactors down

No. of Reactors Down	Probability	Queue Size	Interpretation	Interference/ Cycle
0	$\frac{4}{9}$	0	(No crew required)	0
1	$\frac{2}{9} + \frac{2}{9} = \frac{4}{9}$	0	(Crew attending downed machine —none waiting for service)	0
2	$\frac{1}{9}$	1	(Crew attending one machine and the second must wait)	$(1)(\frac{1}{9})$
				$\frac{1}{9}$ Total

Percent reactor time lost as a result as a result of interference:

$$\frac{\text{Interference}}{\text{Similar Machines}} = \frac{\frac{1}{9}}{2} = \frac{1}{18} = \frac{5.55\%}{\text{Machine}}$$

[3] This is a binomial probability notation. The expression $b(2; 2, \frac{2}{3}) = \frac{4}{9}$ reads: The binomial probability of two successes in two trials, when the probability of success is two in three, equals $\frac{4}{9}$.

As an example, $b(5; 10, \frac{1}{4}) = .0584$, which may be found in any book of mathematical tables that includes a table of individual terms of the binomial distribution.

The values $\frac{4}{9}$, $\frac{4}{9}$, $\frac{1}{9}$ may also be found through the binomial expansion of $(\frac{2}{3} + \frac{1}{3})^2$.

$$\left(\frac{2}{3} + \frac{1}{3}\right)^2 = \left(\frac{2}{3}\right)^2 + \frac{2}{1!}\left(\frac{2}{3}\right)^1\left(\frac{1}{3}\right)^1 + \frac{2\cdot1}{2!}\left(\frac{2}{3}\right)^0\left(\frac{1}{3}\right)^2 = \frac{4}{9} + \frac{4}{9} + \frac{1}{9}$$

Percent down time per machine without interference:[4]

$$\tfrac{1}{3} - \tfrac{1}{18} = \tfrac{5}{18} = 27.78\% \quad \text{of total cycle}$$
or
$$33.33\% - 5.55\% = 27.78\% \quad \text{of total cycle}$$

Percent machine time:

Production Time (% of New Cycle)
$$= (\%TMT)(\%TCT \text{ minus } \% \text{ Interference})^{5,\,6}$$
$$= (66.67\%)(100\% - 5.55\%) = 62.97\%$$

Without interference the reactor would be immediately recycled, once the external work time was completed. If interference exists, however, it should be considered as extending the cycle. This prevents the crew from recycling the reactor and thus reduces machine efficiency. In a complete cycle **with zero interference** one reactor would produce 66.67% of nine hours. Compare this with a situation involving two reactors and 5.55% interference; here each reactor, instead of producing 66.67% of the total cycle, is only producing 94.45% of capacity or (66.67%)(94.45%) = 62.97%.[7]

---

[4] A very important fact must be noted here. Machine interference results in an increased total cycle time, but this affects only the servicing time. The machine cycle will usually remain the same irrespective of the amount of interference per machine. In the situation in which machine time is constant (e.g., numerically controlled), interference cannot extend the machine cycle. An analyst may be deceived in special situations if he is not careful, however, since machine operators may change feeds or speeds to make their operations more rhythmic. Thus, an improper analysis may occur.

In the example of the chemical company, the reaction will always be terminated once the quality-control lab gives authorization. This averages six hours regardless of interference. The reactor may wait, but only for the crew, not for the reaction time. Based on this reasoning, interference is applied only to the service time.

[5] $TCT = 100\%$ which includes interference.

[6] If the original total cycle time equals 100%, then the actual total cycle time is smaller, for it does not include interference. Actual total cycle time is $\% TCT - \%$ Interference.

[7] In the beginning of this computation, the reactor was considered as producing 66.67% of the total cycle. Interference, however, is included in this figure. If there were no interference, then the reactor could produce more batches (Units of Work). So the very fact that interference exists represents lost opportunity of production.

The internal portion of the bar chart changes now that the amount of interference is known.

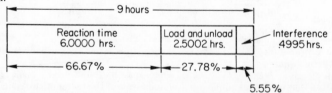

The actual cycle time is 8.5002 hrs compared to the 9 hrs of the original. Machine efficiency now equals 6/8.5002 = 70.59% of the total cycle when interference is excluded. Obviously, interference has reduced total productivity to 66.67/70.59 = 94.45% of its maximum. This is also found when 8.5002/9 = 94.45%. If the reactor is only producing 94.45% of maximum, then its production time is reduced to (66.67%)·(94.45%) = 62.97%.

Remember that the 62.97% does not indicate a decrease in reaction time. If the same formulas of TMT/TCT are used to determine machine efficiency, it will be seen that reaction(machine) time has remained the same. New $TMT = 62.97\%$ and $TCT = 94.45\%$, therefore machine efficiency equals 62.97/94.45 which remains 66.67%.

Using this information it is possible to calculate the productivity of each group of reactors in a similar unit of time. The formula is:

Batches produced Per Unit of Time

$$= (\text{Number of Reactors}) \times (\% \text{ Production Time of One})$$

Two reactors will contribute: $2(62.97\%) = 1.2594$ batches in one unit time.

CALCULATING MACHINE INTERFERENCE FOR THREE REACTORS

Binomial Probability Distribution $= (p + q)^n = (\frac{2}{3} + \frac{1}{3})^3$

Probability Tree

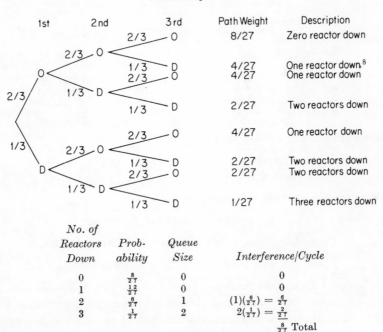

1st	2nd	3rd	Path Weight	Description
		2/3 O	8/27	Zero reactor down
	2/3 O	1/3 D	4/27	One reactor down[8]
		2/3 O	4/27	One reactor down
	1/3 D	1/3 D	2/27	Two reactors down
		2/3 O	4/27	One reactor down
	2/3 O	1/3 D	2/27	Two reactors down
		2/3 O	2/27	Two reactors down
	1/3 D	1/3 D	1/27	Three reactors down

No. of Reactors Down	Probability	Queue Size	Interference/Cycle
0	$\frac{8}{27}$	0	0
1	$\frac{12}{27}$	0	0
2	$\frac{6}{27}$	1	$(1)(\frac{6}{27}) = \frac{6}{27}$
3	$\frac{1}{27}$	2	$2(\frac{1}{27}) = \frac{2}{27}$
			$\frac{8}{27}$ Total

Reactor Time lost as a result of interference:

$$\frac{\text{Interference}}{\text{Similar Machines}} = \frac{\frac{8}{27}}{3} = \frac{8}{81} = \frac{9.88\%}{\text{Machine}}$$

[8] Pr (one reactor down and two are operating) $+ \frac{4}{27} + \frac{4}{27} + \frac{4}{27} = \frac{12}{27}$, which may also be expressed as $b(2; 3, \frac{2}{3})$.

Down time per machine without interference:

$$\tfrac{1}{3} - \tfrac{8}{81} \text{ or } 33.33\% - 9.88\% = \tfrac{19}{81} = 23.46\%$$

Production Time (% of New Total Cycle)

$$= 66.67\%(100\% - 9.88\%) = 60.09\%$$

Batches Produced per Unit Time

$$= \text{(Number of Reactors)(\% Production Time)}$$

$$= (3)(60.09\%) = 1.803 \text{ batches}$$

CALCULATING MACHINE INTERFERENCE FOR FOUR REACTORS

$$(p + q)^n = \left(\frac{2}{3} + \frac{1}{3}\right)^4 = \left(\frac{2}{3}\right)^4 + \frac{4}{1!}\left(\frac{2}{3}\right)^3\left(\frac{1}{3}\right) + \frac{4\cdot 3}{2!}\left(\frac{2}{3}\right)^2\left(\frac{1}{3}\right)^2$$

$$+ \frac{4\cdot 3\cdot 2}{3!}\left(\frac{2}{3}\right)\left(\frac{1}{3}\right)^3 + \frac{4\cdot 3\cdot 2\cdot 1}{4!}\left(\frac{1}{3}\right)^4$$

$$= \frac{16}{81} + \frac{32}{81} + \frac{24}{81} + \frac{8}{81} + \frac{1}{81}$$

No. of Reactors Down	Probability	Queue Size	Interference/Cycle
0	$\tfrac{16}{81}$	0	0
1	$\tfrac{32}{81}$	0	0
2	$\tfrac{24}{81}$	1	$1(\tfrac{24}{81}) = \tfrac{24}{81}$
3	$\tfrac{8}{81}$	2	$2(\tfrac{8}{81}) = \tfrac{16}{81}$
4	$\tfrac{1}{81}$	3	$3(\tfrac{1}{81}) = \tfrac{3}{81}$
			Total $= \tfrac{43}{81}$

Reactor time lost as a result of interference:

$$\frac{\text{Interference}}{\text{Similar Machine}} = \frac{\tfrac{43}{81}}{4} = \frac{43}{324} = \frac{13.24\%}{\text{Machine}}$$

Down time per machine without interference:

$$\tfrac{1}{3} - \tfrac{43}{324} \text{ or } 33.33\% - 13.24\% = 20.09\%$$

$$\% \text{ Production Time} = 66.67\%(100\% - 13.24\%) = 57.84\%$$

$$\text{Batches Produced} = 4(57.84\%) = 2.314 \text{ batches}$$

Table 2.1 shows that two reactors with a ratio of $\tfrac{1}{3}$ down and $\tfrac{2}{3}$ operating will be restricted to producing 1.26 batches in any 100% unit time, when compared with other combinations of reactors in the same time interval, because of interference.[9]

This comparison shows that the lowest cost per unit is $122.00, which

[9] When working with small cycle times this is usually described as pieces per hour. For example: Four machines with a 95% actual production time equals $4(95\%) = 3.80$ pieces in the time period specified, i.e., 3.8 min., 3.8/hr., or 3.8/day.

ensues when one crew operates three reactors. The costs here are very close, but greater differences may be expected for other ratios of man-to-machine time.[10]

Table 2.1

COST COMPARISONS
(Using one hour as the base time for comparison purposes)
Given: Labor Cost = $25/hr, and Reactor Cost = $65/hr

Number of Reactors	% of Cycle Available for Reaction	Total* Produc- tivity	Labor Cost (Hour)	Machine Cost (Hour)	Cost Comparisons
1	66.67%	0.667	$25	1($65)	$\frac{\$25 + \$65}{.667} = \$134.9$
2	62.97%	1.259	$25	2($65)	$\frac{\$25 + \$130}{1.259} = \$123.9$
3	60.09%	1.803	$25	3($65)	$\frac{\$25 + \$195}{1.803} = \$122.0$
4	57.84%	2.314	$25	4($65)	$\frac{\$25 + \$260}{2.314} = \$123.2$

*This is batches produced in a unit of time. The column therefore represents a ratio of productivity for one, two, three, and four reactors in any unit of time.

2.43 Probabilistic Analysis (with service times not including interference)

In the previous example all that was known was the down time and machine time. The forthcoming examples, however, deal with situations in which service and machine times are known.

A binomial model may again be used, but more accuracy can be found through use of graphs created by mathematicians explicitly for this purpose. (See Figs. 2.5 and 2.6.)

These graphs are based on random machine down time with either constant or exponentially distributed service times.[11]

[10] A question may be raised about the cost figures for one reactor as it can be calculated that the one crew–one reactor cost per batch = (25 + 65)9 = $810. Why the $134.9? Elaboration of the topic may clarify this point. It is not essential to compare all segments of the cycle. Only those that are affected need be considered. This comparison was made with respect to lost opportunity to produce; the diminishing machine percentages reflect how interference has affected each combination with the hand time of load and unload remaining constant. The hand time is not essential in this comparison and thus has been factored out. One reactor had a productivity of 0.667, so without interference three reactors should produce 3(.667) = 2.001. But interference has reduced the productivity of three reactors to 1.803. Thus (1.803/2.001)(134.9) = $122.

[11] Consider a packaging machine—it may automatically stop for various reasons: material exhausted, overweight, underweight, supply of packages depleted, printing smeared, machine breakdown, and numerous others. There is little chance of predicting these since they follow no schedule. If we assume that each event occurs independently, a random demand for service is created.

Figure 2.5

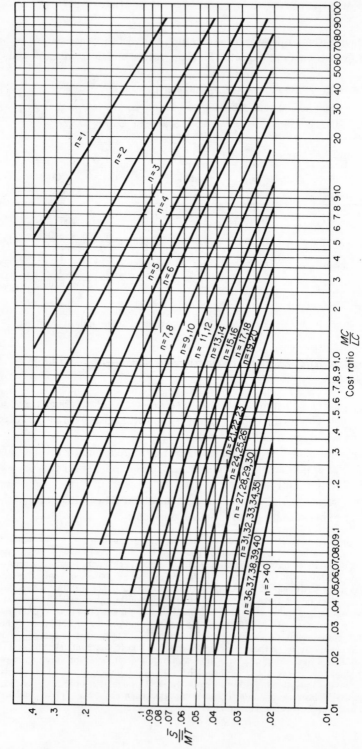

Optimum machine assignment — (random machine down time and exponentially distributed service times)

Source: E. H. Bowman and R. B. Fetter, *Analyses of Industrial Operations*, Richard D. Irwin, Homewood, Illinois, 1959. By permission of the publisher.

Figure 2.6

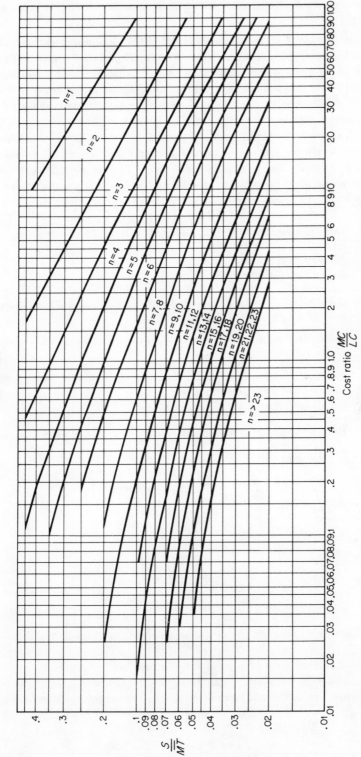

Optimum machine assignment — (random machine down time and constant service time)

Source: E. H. Bowman and R. B. Fetter, *Analyses of Industrial Operations*, Richard D. Irwin, Homewood, Illinois, 1959. By permission of the publisher.

The concept that service time may be either random or constant is difficult to envision since analysts have found random labor time distributions even in the most routine jobs. Yet while it is hard to find a constant service time, it is mathematically possible and should be included in the analysis. Another reason, which may be called for intuitively, is that jobs especially adaptable to sychronous servicing, even though having a distribution, have exceptionally small standard deviations, which means that servicing events hover in greater proportion around the mean. *A constant situation by definition has no standard deviation. Thus it may be seen that while constant service is a rarity, an analyst may be better off using a constant service approach in those cases with small standard deviations for service times.*

To use these graphs, the following information must be accumulated.

MC = Machine cost per unit time

LC = Labor cost per unit time

$\bar{S}$ = Random Service Times, S = Constant Service Times

$\overline{MT}$ = Machine time–average time (constant cycle plus average delays) Service on a first come–first served basis

$\dfrac{S}{MT}$ = Ratio of constant service time to average machine time (both expressed in same unit times)

$\dfrac{\bar{S}}{MT}$ = Ratio of average service time to average machine time (both expressed in same unit times)

$\dfrac{MC}{LC}$ = Ratio of machine cost to labor costs

n = Optimum number of machines to assign crew (one or more workers)

Use of graph: (Fig. 2.6)

MC = \$25/hr

LC = \$5/hr

$\bar{S}$ = 4 min

$\overline{MT}$ = 100 min

$\dfrac{MC}{LC} = 5$

$\dfrac{\bar{S}}{MT} = .04$

n = 7 or 8 (read from Fig. 2.6)

If MC/LC had been 20, then the optimum machine assignment would have been five.

Random service time was used for the previous example. However, if service time were constant, then the optimum machine assignment as determined by Fig. 2.5 would have been nine or ten machines. Here it may be seen that predictability increased the machine assignment. It may therefore be recommended that operator assignments be simplified to minimize variations in work routines, since this allows for larger machine assignments.

2.5 SUMMARY

A number of machine-interference problems have been discussed and calculated to show the effect of waiting time. To infer, however, that an analyst may simply use these techniques per se would be incorrect since there are too many variables not covered in the current mathematical approaches. For example, random calls for service may be incorrect when one man has the responsibility for only two machines. Actually the probabilities of finding that perfect situation are so remote that a question may be raised about the use of quantitative techniques for decision making.

It is important that attention again be drawn to the concept of mathematics as a way of thinking rather than doing. Most assuredly the available mathematical techniques cannot be fashioned to fit a given situation exactly. What can be substituted for them? Experience? Intuition? It is offered here that mathematics while not perfectly fitting many real-life business or industrial situations will give a substantial enrichment of understanding about the topic or project being studied. This greater understanding will improve the probabilities of deciding correctly and thus is justification for using mathematical analysis in the decision-making process.

2.6 DISCUSSION AND REVIEW QUESTIONS

1. Machine interference presents many serious problems. List these important problem areas; then, using a step-by-step process, describe how you would approach a complex interference situation.

2. How would you overcome the coldness of a mathematical approach to interference problems when it must be explained to the union committee?

3. Use the binomial process to predict the optimum machine assignment when average times are: Total Machine Time $= \frac{1}{2}$ hour, Total Down Time (interference included) $= \frac{1}{6}$ hour, Labor Cost $= \$3/\text{hr}$, and Machine Cost $= \$12/\text{hr}$. Check these results using the optimum machine assignment graph (Fig. 2.6). Why are the results different? (*Hint:* try to develop a method of subtracting interference from down time to arrive at average service time.)

4. If $\bar{S} = 8$ and $\overline{MT} = 6$, this ratio cannot be found on the graph. Why?

5. Justify the fact that as the ratio of MC/LC gets larger the machine assignment gets smaller.

6. Dependency of the second machine on the first is a commonly found type of interference problem. Consider this example: the first of two semiautomatic turret lathes grips a forged steel ring by the inside diameter and machines the outside diameter and face. The second machine uses the previously machined surfaces to grip the ring and subsequently machines the inside diameter and the other face. The product is now symmetrically machined and will pass rigorous quality tests. This operation between lathes is set up to have almost identical machine cycle times thereby minimizing artificially-created interference. The operator has the responsibilities of the external hand time of loading and unloading, in addition to the internal hand time of pre-positioning material, clearing chips, gauging finished parts, and other responsibilities. From this description it may be seen that the segments of the total cycle for one machine are constant (machine time) and random (operator time). Dependency relationships are usually associated with a station-to-station simulation problem which is readily applicable to queuing theory. See Chapter 6. Assume that both machines have a two-minute machining cycle but that operator times vary from a mean value which is one minute per machine. How much is each cycle expanded due to interference? Remember that the second cannot operate unless it receives a part from machine number one or unless it has an inventory of pieces. Would it be wise to begin the day with an inventory of pieces at machine number two? If so, how many?

7. Determine the number of machines one operator can economically service if labor cost = \$5/hr and machine costs = \$15/hr. Consider that machine time, internal service time, and external service time are distributed as follows:

Machine Time	Occurrences
.50 min	14
1.00	95
1.50	230
2.00	315
2.50	234
3.00	97
3.50	12

Internal Service Time	Occurrences
.0　min	13
.25	27
.50	29
.75	18
1.00	9
1.25	5
1.50	1
1.75	1

External Service Time	Occurrences
.20 min	2
.40	10
.60	21
.80	27
1.00	23
1.20	12
1.40	5
1.60	2
1.80	1
2.00	1

8. Using the data in problem seven, what would be the optimum man-to-machine assignment when an operator works at 130% incentive pace?

9. If the machine time were constant in problem seven, how would this affect the number of machines possible for one operator to run?

10. A Case History of Machine Interference within a Metal Working Industry

A company has forty-eight single-spindle automatic screw machines and has one operator assigned to each group of six machines. The machines are equipped with automatic shut-offs and signal lights to reduce major breakdowns and minimize interference. The lights draw the operator's attention to the downed machines, as the area is extremely noisy and many minutes could elapse before the downed machine received attention. The operator may be engaged in major work on one machine when the light signals that another has stopped. He will immediately give attention to the newly-downed machine to determine the extent of its problem. If the problem is a minor one, he will rectify it rather than make it wait in queue until he finishes a major repair. There are many such interruptions during the course of a major repair, and studies show that many of these would have been avoided if he had not been engaged in other work. *Minor repairs, therefore, increase as a function of reduced attention time.*

The operator also has the responsibility for: supplying the machine with material, clearing chips from the tool area, moving the tote pan of completed parts to conveyor, changing tools when they are broken, testing pieces on a random basis, and many other things. He has a group incentive, and the company anticipates that his earnings will be thirty percent above base rate. Historical data show that incentive earnings have a considerable fluctuation.

The inability to predict daily productivity accurately is felt in many departments throughout the company. Cost accounting has difficulty in assigning proper standard costs for each piece because costs for the same part vary greatly with each order. Production control similarly experiences difficulties as it cannot accurately predict the total number of pieces. The operator's attitude fluctuates with the orders as do his incentive earnings. Inventory levels and delivery dates also suffer.

The problem becomes so acute that the industrial engineering department assigns time-study men many weeks of around-the-clock eight-hour time studies to ascertain the difficulties and determine the machine interference. Using this and other data, mathematical formulas that include hand time, machine time, allowances, and delays are developed for each part made on these machines. It is found, however, that the problem still prevails and complaints again mount.

In an attempt to alleviate the problem, management studies the tool-change aspect of the job and determines that it is advisable to change all tools every four hours regardless of their condition. They determine that this action will minimize the interference that develops between machines as a result of tool breakage and adjustment. Tool problems get priority attention from the operator, and a trip to the centralized tool crib is required if a tool is broken. Each machine has seven tools, and the adjustment of one usually means the adjustment of all. Queues develop at the tool crib as the operator seeks new tools, and the situation is not substantially relieved by giving this department a tool-crib priority. It is expected that the new tool-change policy will relieve the problem, and this is documented through preliminary data.

When the machine operator is at the tool crib a relief operator will maintain his machines. Often, however, the relief operator is not available because he is assisting another. This could result in five additional machines being downed because no one is available to service them.

The whole crew, set-up men, relief men, and operators share in a group-incentive plan. They will assist each other as much as possible whenever a downed-machine situation occurs. It is not unusual to find the operators from both sides of the downed series of machines assuming responsibilities for the remaining ones that are operational. This means that at intervals throughout the day an operator may be responsible for six, eight, or nine machines. There is a continual request for additional relief men, but management is hesitant.

Of the six machines within one operator's jurisdiction each may be producing different, similar, or a combination of products. Expanding this possible grouping throughout forty-eight machines can easily show the magnitude of the available combinations.

The company retains a labor-relations consultant to evaluate the problem, and in his report he states:

> "Mathematical predictions of the interference and queues may prove expensive and subject to error. Yet, while not fitting exactly, they may provide guidelines to the magnitude of the problem and may be more representative than actual time studies.

> The coldness of a mathematical approach may often upset laborers.

Mathematicians, operations research specialists, and engineers very often spend months in research to develop great accuracy only to find an unreceptive audience during the presentation of data. This lack of understanding by the laboring group may result in management's agreeing to excessive safety factors in the form of delays, allowances, etc."

Phil Carrol describes this dilemma: "We carry out labor and material costs to the fourth decimal place. But we spread the overhead with a shovel."[12]

The lack of understanding by both management and especially labor may cause a jaundiced acceptance of this solution. Usually pressure by labor and first-line supervision forces management to succumb to excessive safety factors in the form of increased allowances. This upsets the research group. It must be impressed on the industrial scientist, however, that possibly as much time should be spent on the behavioralistic aspect of a project as is spent in scientific research. *If not, a meaningful project may be abused by those who do not understand.*

The problem continues and a grievance is filed by the union. It is their contention that incentive opportunities in this department are not similar to those in other departments throughout the company. To improve their incentive opportunities they recommend the use of two additional relief men and that one operator should have the responsibilities of only four machines.

Management's scientific study conclusively shows that the operators should easily make thirty percent above base rate, and that the present operating conditions are correct; yet the union will not accept this, and the workers are in a slowdown.

How would you, as production manager, approach this problem?

[12] Carrol, Phil, *Better Wage Incentives* (New York: McGraw-Hill Book Company, Inc., 1957).

3. Mathematical Queuing Models

This chapter is divided into two basic learning categories: queuing formulas (with introductory examples), and mathematical derivations. It was designed in this manner to satisfy the needs of a wide set of users. A consideration of the first category may be all that time allows especially when this book is supplementary to many others. This alone, however, will provide a basic understanding. The second category contains the majority of mathematical proofs for those rudimentary formulas utilized throughout this chapter. Both areas are taken in order of increasing difficulty. This design allows the reader to progress according to his own desires or abilities and does not sacrifice the conceptual aspect of queuing theory.

It is strongly recommended, however, that the reader at least work through the basic one-line, one-server development as given in Secs. 3.71 and 3.72. This will improve his knowledge of the theories underlying the subject, and thus broaden his understanding of queuing theory.

3.2 PROBABILITY AND QUEUING THEORY

On May 29, 1940, a B. B. C. announcer conceivably reported: "The troops are queued up on the beach at Dunkirk, and all available ships are required for the purpose of evacuation." Authorities estimated that three hundred and fifty thousand combat soldiers were evacuated even though the odds of success were extremely poor. Why the success? Could it have been luck? Most assuredly events would have to have fallen just right; but is this not the essence of probabilities? When odds are quoted, or the most likely (average) situation is given, an implication follows—the chances that something else will eventually occur are axiomatic.

When queues are treated using mathematical analysis, they are also based on averages. This can similarly result in a chance event since any solution based on expected value indicates only what may be anticipated. In other words, the majority of events will hover around a mean value. This does not negate, but in fact predicts, the eventuality of a remote, possibly undesired, happening. Within this framework of uncertainty a manager must weigh his utility for such an eventuality and act accordingly.

Utility values for similar events may not be equal, when one environment is measured against another. For example, the value assigned to a stalled engine is quite different for automotive engineers as compared to aeronautical engineers, and four people waiting in line may have distinctly different utility values for the hospital administrator as against a college administrator. Assume that probabilities are equal—Pr (stalled engine) $= \frac{17}{10,000}$. This may be wholly acceptable to the automotive engineer although wholly unacceptable to the aeronautical engineer. Also, Pr (four in waiting line) $= \frac{1}{10}$ will be rejected by a hospital administrator as not being reasonably safe when human life is involved.

The following sections will show how to measure most characteristics associated with waiting lines. Some attempt is made through examples to show the effect of utility value on the decision-making process; but again, it must be emphasized that these are individualistic, and may not fit values of other people. Studies have shown, however, that without an objective study that assigns probabilities to the various events, managers will over compensate. This fact further justifies such mathematical studies as queuing theory.

3.3 CHARACTERISTICS OF MATHEMATICAL QUEUING MODELS

In Chapter 1 queues were classified as One Line–One Server, One Line–Multiple Server, Multiple Line–Multiple Server, and Station-to-Station models. They were also cross-classified by allowing the arrivals or service to be either random or constant. To compound things even further, it was necessary to consider which one of many disciplines held. Two of the more common questions an analyst usually considers are: Will the arrivals be served on a first come–first served basis? Do arrivals with priorities go to the front of the line for *immediate* service?

Numerous situations were described in Chapter 1 showing that lines developed when input exceeded output rates. These conditions leave the analyst with many decision areas, the primary one being: should the system have a waiting line? Analysts usually find that a waiting line for service is an economic necessity. Thus complex problems arise from a search for the best combination of waiting times and service times.

There are sociological, psychological, economic, and many other factors that influence waiting lines. These were also explored in Chapter 1. Assuming that an analyst may control input, output, or both, what factors concerning the line are necessary for a good decision? He may find that, economically, a line should be ten elements in length, but if this line involves people they may balk at a long waiting time. Therefore in the decision process both length of the line and time in the system are important.

To emphasize this further: assume that a hopper contains ten thousand ball bearings and that the whole hopper vibrates in order to allow a bearing to drop through an exit hole in the bottom. If the number of bearings dropping in one minute intervals were counted, it might be found that 1st min. equals eleven bearings, 2nd = 9, 3rd = 15, 4 = 8, 5 = 12, etc. The arithmetical mean (expected value) of these data could be found by adding the individual values and dividing by the observations; but remember that this only represents an average. Now consider that these bearings drop on to a conveyor and are processed at an average rate of fifteen per minute. If the average arrival rate (bearings feeding from this vibrator) were eleven per minute, there would theoretically be no line, as the servicing capacity is greater than the input. Still, a line would form. Why?

The input and output data represent averages.[1] These averages may come, however, from a very wide or narrow distribution.[2] Thus at random intervals of time, output may exceed input, or input may exceed output. If the latter occurs, then a waiting line forms and will not clear until sufficient intervals have occurred where output is greater than input. The system

---

[1] The arithmetic mean is defined as: $\bar{x}_i = (1/n) \sum\limits_{i=1}^{n} x_i$. In this usage, x_i indicates individual arrival rates (input to the system). Thus, $\bar{x}_i$ equals average arrivals, which in queuing theory is designated as (λ). Similarly, y_i indicates individual service rates. In queuing theory $\bar{y}_i = (\mu)$.

[2] A distribution is made up of numerous individual events, and the sum of their weights (values) divided by the number of events results in the mean, arithmetic average, which is the measure of central tendency used in most mathematical queuing formulas. The nature of a distribution stems from individual events greater than, less than, or equal to the average. Consider what happens when *individual events* of two distributions are combined as is found in queuing molels in which input (x_i) and output (y_i) have separate and distinct distributions. There are $\binom{3}{2}$ possibilities: arrival rates greater than servicing rates, arrival rates equal to service rates, and arrival rates less than service rates. These may be expressed as $(x/y) > 1$, $(x/y) = 1$, and $(x/y) < 1$ respectively. Any combination of these may occur, which could result in a run on the system. If a series of individual $(x/y) > 1$ events follows in sequence, a line forms and grows in size. This will continue until there is a series $(x/y) < 1$ events following in a large enough sequence to eliminate the line. The number of events required to clear the line is dependent on the ratio of the individual (x/y)'s. The nature of the original data indicates that the line will eventually clear when averages are reached and maintained. Another important feature to remember is that service cannot be inventoried for future use. In a series of events where $[(x/y) < 1, (x/y) < 1, (x/y) < 1, (x/y) > 1]$ a line has formed at the concluding event even though preceded by numerous events with excessive clearing capacity. Contrast this to a series of individual events $[(x/y) > 1, (x/y) > 1, (x/y) > 1, (x/y) < 1]$ where a line here will form provided that the three preceding individual events have created a waiting line greater than the last event's excess capacity to clear.

unquestionably has a clearing capacity, but when the ratio of average input to average output approaches 1, there is greater difficulty in clearing the system. Symbolically the average input to the system (arrivals per minute, hour, day, or other unit time) is designated as λ (lambda), and the average output of the system (service rate or rate at which inputs are cleared) is designated as μ (mu). Thus the ratio of lambda to mu (λ/μ) is the clearing ratio of the system. This clearing ratio is usually shown by mathematicians as P (rho), where $P = \lambda/\mu$. If $\lambda/\mu > 1$, then the average arrival rate is greater than the average service rate, which loosely means that the waiting line will grow without bound. If $P > 1$, the system may be designed with more servicing stations (designated as S), or the arrival or servicing rates may be altered, depending on which of these three possibilities are within the analyst's control. When additional service stations are required, this is called a multiple server situation, which has the restriction that $\lambda/S\mu < 1$. This means that a multiple server situation has a total average servicing capacity greater than the average arrival rate.

The intricacies of why a line forms have been explored. The question that now must be asked, given that a line will form, is what other characteristics must be evaluated to give the analyst greater understanding? If the line is evaluated at random time intervals, it will be found that it may be classified as having zero, few, or numerous elements. It may be further classified with respect to time; for example, an element waits a short time, long time, or is immediately processed. Rather than evaluate each individual event or combination, the analyst knows that these too will approach an average. Thus mathematicians have developed formulas, for the analyst's use, to determine the expected length of the waiting line, the expected time in line, the expected number being serviced plus waiting, and the expected time in the system.

An illustration of this may clarify the fundamental points (page 49).

As the distant person (element) approaches the line, immediate questions are raised: "How long will the line be when I get there (E_w)? How many are in the system (E_n)? How long must I wait for service (E_t)?" If this approaching person cannot see the line, then only averages or probabilities can be used to answer his questions. For example: "You may expect to find four people in line;" There is a probability of $\frac{1}{3}$, Pr (0.333), of finding only two people in the system." Figure 3.1 illustrates the expected situation, when the ratio λ/μ is known. It is important again to emphasize that many trials make up an average. In a real-life situation the approaching element will encounter various line sizes. If this trip is repeated a number of times, then his expectation is found by adding the results of each experiment and dividing by the number of trials.

The previous questions could have been expressed differently. For example: What is the probability that the system is completely clear so that

Figure 3.1

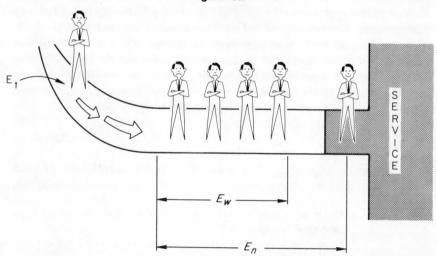

I will get immediate service $P_0(t)$?[3] What is the probability that only two people will be in line and that another is receiving service $P_3(t)$? In general, what is the probability of any number being before me $P_n(t)$?[4] These probabilities assign values to specific cases with the $\sum\limits_{n=0}^{\infty} nP_n(t) = (0P_0 + 1P_1 + 2P_2 + \ldots) = E_n$

In the preceding discussion, the characteristics of the line were reviewed with respect to a specialized illustration. From a broader base, it is found that

$$E_w = \text{The expected length of the waiting line}$$

takes on a number of meanings. It can mean the conveyor length required before a packaging machine, the item to minimize when planning a supermarket, or a critical item when considering filters in a chemical operation

---

[3] In Fig. 3.1, the notation $P_0(t)$ indicates the probability that an arrival would get immediate service because there are zero units in the system at time (t). $P_0(t)$ increases as λ/μ approaches zero. The formula for $P_0(t) = 1 - (\lambda/\mu)$, so, as λ/μ approaches zero, $P_0(t)$ approaches one, which in probability notation indicates that the event in question will occur with certainty. This means that an arrival will get immediate service. Conversely, as λ/μ approaches one, $P_0(t)$ approaches zero. The value of $P_0(t) = 1 - (\lambda/\mu)$ is governed by the ratio λ/μ and has limiting values of zero and one, which is characteristic of a probabilistic value.

[4] The probability of one, two, three units in the system at time (t) is designated as $P_1(t)$, $P_2(t)$, and $P_3(t)$ respectively. Thus the designation for any value is given as $P_n(t)$, where n represents any value for which probabilities are sought. The size of n is unrestricted in an infinite universe, but in a finite universe it is restricted to its finite limits m. To find the probability of five units in the system at time (t), substitute five for n in the formulas $P_n(t) = (\lambda/\mu)^n P_0(t)$, or $P_5(t) = (\lambda/\mu)^5 P_0(t)$.

because too large a queue at the filter will affect the blending processes. E_n, E_Ψ, and E_t are approached the same way in every problem, yet they too may have substantially different meanings. The expected time in line E_t is critical when considering items that degenerate or change over time, while it is a desirable feature for items that improve with ageing. E_n (the expected number being serviced plus waiting) and E_Ψ (the expected time in the system) may be causing a loss of customers, decreased machine efficiency, and incorrect assembly line planning, when considered individually or jointly.

3.4 GLOSSARY OF GENERAL TERMS

$\mu =$ Mean service rate—average number serviced in one unit of time (per channel).

$\lambda =$ Mean arrival rate—average number arriving in one unit of time.

$\dfrac{\lambda}{\mu} =$ Clearing ratio (if $\mu > \lambda$, then capacity to serve is greater than demand for service).

$n =$ Number of units in the system (waiting or being serviced).

P or $Pr =$ Probability Notation.

$P_0(t) =$ Probability of "zero" units in the system at time t. An input will receive immediate service.

$P_3(t) =$ Probability of "three" units in the system at time t. An input must wait for service until these three have been cleared.

$P_n(t) =$ Probability of n units in the system at time t designated as P_n for a finite universe and $P_n(t)$ for an infinite universe.

$P_m =$ Probability of m elements in service or demanding service.

$w =$ Length of waiting line not including those being serviced.

$E =$ Expected value $\sum\limits_{i=0}^{\infty} P_i N_i$

$E_w =$ Expected (average) length of waiting line.

$E_0 =$ Expected number that have not departed a finite universe for service.

$E_n =$ Expected number being serviced plus waiting.

$E_s =$ Expected number being serviced.

$E_t =$ Expected time in line (average time the arriving element must wait before being serviced).

$E_e =$ Expected utilization of s.

$E_\Psi =$ Expected time in system (E_t plus the average time required for service).

$m =$ Total universe supplying input to the system. The universe is either infinite or finite. A finite universe is usually a small countable set of machines, machinists, objects, etc. Each universe has its own distinct formulas. Infinite formulas are used when the arrivals come from an infinite source or a large finite population.

s = Number of servers ... which equals one in single line—single server cases, and more than one in single line—multiple server cases.

$m\lambda$ = Maximum expected arrivals in a unit time when the universe is finite, none having departed for service (usually noted at λ).[5]

$(m - n)\lambda$ = Maximum expected arrivals when n units are either in line or awaiting service. This shows a dependency relationship which is characteristic of a finite set $[(m - n)\lambda = \lambda_n]$.

3.5 POISSON DISRIBUTION—AN INTUITIVE APPROACH

3.51 Analysis of Normal, Poisson, and Exponential Distribution

The *normal distribution* measures values throughout the range of x, which means that it may take on an infinite number of values; for this reason it is called a continuous distribution. It has the following basic properties: a single peak with the function of x, $f(x)$, falling off continually on either side; it is symmetrical about the mean, where the mean is described as the balancing point of the distribution; the continuous curve representing the normal distribution is convexed upward as the value of x approaches the mean, but at a distance from the mean the curve changes directions and is concave upward, the curve thus assuming the shape of a bell. Mathematically the normal curve has:

$$\text{Range of } x: -\infty \text{ to } \infty$$

$$\text{Mean}: \bar{x} = \mu$$

$$\text{Variance } X: = \sigma^2$$

and the equation of the normal curve

$$f(x) = \frac{1}{\sigma\sqrt{2\pi}} \, e^{-(x-\mu)^2/(2\sigma^2)}$$

The *Poisson distribution* counts values throughout the range of x. It is a discrete distribution that has a positive probability that the variable x equals zero. For example if x counts the number of patrons arriving at a ticket booth every fifteen minutes, then according to the Poisson probability laws there exists a possibility that zero patrons will arrive. Thus arrivals to a

---

[5] When $m\lambda$ and $(m - n)\lambda$ are substituted into Equation 15 of the infinite mathematical proof, the finite queuing model is developed. With these conditions, service demands become: $\mu_0 = 0$ and $\mu_n = \mu$. These are based on the restriction that $(\lambda/\mu) < 1$.

ticket booth during a prescribed interval may vary from zero to infinity. Contrast this to a normal distribution where theoretically zero arrivals does not occur. The Poisson distribution has these basic properties: a single peak; values of x less than the mean fall off in probabilistic values at a rate dissimilar to its equidistant counterpart which is greater than the mean; it is not symmetrical about the mean, and it has more values of x greater than the mean. Mathematically the Poisson distribution has: Range of x: 0, 1, 2, 3, 4, . . . , ∞; Mean: $x = \lambda$, Variance: $x = \lambda$, and the equation of the Poisson distribution is:

$$P(x) = \frac{\lambda^x e^{-\lambda}}{x!}$$

Thus the Poisson distribution is skewed when the mean, λ, assumes small values, and it always intersects the $y = f(x)$ axis at e^{-x}.

The *exponential distribution* measures values throughout the range of x, thus as in the normal distribution it is classified as continuous. In queuing theory service is continuous and is characterized by the exponential distribution. This, as the Poisson distribution, yields values for the probability that x assumes values of zero. As x decreases, the function of x increases, given that x is positive and the curve negatively sloped. Thus $f(x)$ is greatest when $x = 0$. Mathematically: Range of $x = 0 - \infty$, Mean of $x = 1/a$, Variance of x: $= 1/a^2$, and the formula for a negative exponential distribution is $f(x) = ae^{-ax}$.

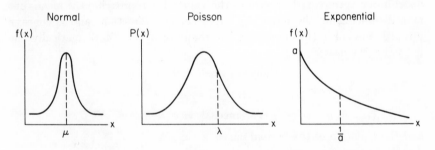

3.52 Relationship of Poisson and Exponential Distribution

To develop mathematical queuing formulas the Poisson distribution is used to characterize the arrivals of people and the exponential distribution their servicing.[6a] Thus there is a correspondence of the arrival and servicing distributions. The Poisson distribution has a mean of λ, and since this depicts

[6a] The distribution of real-world data rarely follows the classical Poisson-exponential model. The mathematics for relationship between other distributions is laborious at best, and was thus limited in its usefulness. Mathematicians knew that these other relationships could be simulated, but this was too laborious and costly until the advent of the modern electronic computing machines.

the input to a queuing system the arrival rate similarly is λ. Service, while continuous, is dependent on the arrivals because zero arrivals equal zero service, given no waiting line. If the mean arrival rate is λ, the interarrival time is $1/\lambda$. For example if $\lambda = 5$ per min, then the time between arrivals is $1/\lambda = \frac{1}{5}$ min. Using $1/\lambda$ as the mean, the Poisson formula for interarrivals becomes $\lambda e^{-\lambda x}$, which is the exponential formula previously given except with $\lambda = a$.

3.6 SET UP AND SOLUTION OF VARIOUS QUEUING PROBLEMS

The formulas used in these solutions are introduced without proof. Included in Sec. 3.7, however, are the majority of mathematical proofs for those who wish to delve further into queuing theory.

The usual procedure followed when setting up the majority of queuing problems is to: (a) make certain that data gathered are representative and do not constitute a specialized case; (b) list the data used in solving the problem; (c) express λ (the mean arrival rate) and μ (the mean service rate) *in equivalent terms*, i.e., minutes, hours, days, years, etc.; (d) determine whether input data come from a finite or infinite population; (e) include in detail only those areas necessary for decision making when the project is presented to management in its final form.[6b]

3.61 One Line—One Server (Infinite Population)

General Formulas

1. $P_0(t) = 1 - \dfrac{\lambda}{\mu} = Pr$ $\left\{\begin{array}{l}\text{Zero units in the system when the rate of} \\ \text{arrival } \lambda \text{ and the service } \mu \text{ are given.}\end{array}\right\}$

2. $P_n(t) = \left(\dfrac{\lambda}{\mu}\right)^n P_0(t) = \left(\dfrac{\lambda}{\mu}\right)^n\left(1 - \dfrac{\lambda}{\mu}\right) = Pr$ $\left\{\begin{array}{l}n \text{ units in queue plus} \\ \text{being serviced.}\end{array}\right\}$

3. $E_n = \dfrac{\lambda}{\mu - \lambda} = $ Expected number being serviced plus waiting.

4. $E_w = \dfrac{\lambda^2}{\mu(\mu - \lambda)} = $ Expected number in queue—(length of waiting line not including those being serviced).

5. $E_t = \dfrac{E_w}{\lambda} = \dfrac{\lambda}{\mu(\mu - \lambda)} = $ Expected waiting time in line.

6. $E_\Psi = E_t + \dfrac{1}{\mu} = \dfrac{1}{\mu - \lambda} = $ Expected waiting time in system.

[6b] Often when a project is presented it contains too many preliminary data. This sometimes discourages management, which may cause a meaningful project to be abused.

7. $P(N > n) = \left(\dfrac{\lambda}{\mu}\right)^{n+1} = Pr$ (The number in the waiting line plus the number being serviced is greater than n.)[7]

Restrictions: (a) First Come–First Served Discipline.

(b) $\dfrac{\lambda}{\mu} < 1$, often called the Traffic Intensity or Clearing Ratio. This restriction must hold, otherwise $P_n(t)$ is not independent of (t).

EXAMPLE 1. A service station has pumps for both gasoline-and diesel-powered vehicles. Of its four pumps one is diesel. Two trucks cannot be serviced simultaneously although two diesel fuels are carried. Studies show that truck arrivals at this one pump follow a Poisson distribution with a mean of ten trucks per hour, while service is exponentially distributed with a mean of twenty per hour.[8] Find E_n, E_w, and E_t and E_Ψ.

From this information it is found that:

$\lambda = 10$ arrivals per hour[9]
$\mu = 20$ services per hour[10]
$\lambda/\mu = \frac{1}{2}$, which satisfy the restriction of $\lambda/\mu < 1$.[11]

---

[7] $P(N > n)$ when $n = 0$ $\therefore$ $P(N > 0) = P(1 - P_0) = \dfrac{\lambda}{\mu}$;

$P(N > 1) = P[1 - (P_0 + P_1)] = 1 - \left[1 - \dfrac{\lambda}{\mu} + \dfrac{\lambda}{\mu}\left(1 - \dfrac{\lambda}{\mu}\right)\right] = \left(\dfrac{\lambda}{\mu}\right)^2$; etc.

An illustration may broaden understanding. A truck operator knows from experience that his produce will perish if he must wait for more than two others to unload. Here, instead of being interested in P_2 (the probability of two trucks in the system), he is interested in $P(N > 2)$ (the probability of more than two trucks in the system).

[8] Mathematical queuing formulas are based on Poisson arrivals and exponential service. The formulas will not readily hold if input, outputs, or both do not follow these restrictions. Queuing problems having other or not easily defined distributions are best solved through simulation techniques, as described in Chapter 6. More information about the Poisson and exponential distributions is included in the mathematical derivations. See Sec. 3.7.

[9] Ten elements arrive from an *infinite universe* for service. These arrivals are not equally spaced or paced—all we know is that an average of ten arrive per hour and that arrivals follow a Poisson distribution.

[10] The servicing ability is twenty per hour for one pump. This is an average which means that at varying intervals, service time may be greater or smaller than the average. The fundamental demand on service is that the distribution be exponential.

[11] λ and μ are based on averages. Thus $(\lambda/\mu) < 1$ is also based on averages. The nature of an average dictates there are times when individual occurences of (input/output) > 1 and (input/output) $\rightarrow 0$. For example: ten elements are expected, but the nature of the distribution, with λ as its mean, indicates that the input could be greater or less than what is expected. The system can expect to service twenty, but again this will vary greatly during individual trials. Consider that we have twenty arrivals, which is a possibility, and that we can only service eight, which similarly is a possibility; arrivals then exceed capacity, and a line forms. This holds true for any time interval, unit time, and is not restricted to a one-hour period. This variable input, combined with variable output, is a description of what happens when two averages are combined. These variations allow a line to build during one time interval, and similarly allow it to be depleted during another time interval.

The expected number being serviced plus waiting is:

$$E_n = \frac{\lambda}{(\mu - \lambda)} = \frac{10}{(20 - 10)} = \frac{10}{10} = 1 \quad \text{truck}$$

The expected number in queue—length of waiting line not including those being serviced is:

$$E_w = \frac{\lambda^2}{\mu(\mu - \lambda)} = \frac{10^2}{20(20 - 10)} = \frac{100}{20(10)} = \frac{100}{200} = \frac{1}{2} \quad \text{truck}$$

The expected waiting time in line is:

$$E_t = \frac{E_w}{\lambda} = \frac{\frac{1}{2}}{10} = \frac{1}{20} \quad \text{of an hour per truck}$$

The expected waiting time in the system is:

$$E_\Psi = E_t + \frac{1}{\mu} = \frac{1}{20} + \frac{1}{20} = \frac{2}{20} = \frac{1}{10} \quad \text{of an hour per truck.}$$

EXAMPLE 2.   Table 3.1 shows the quantity of boats and barges processed monthly by an Ohio River dam.

Table 3.1

ACTUAL DATA

	"Lockages"*	"Straight Throughs"**
January	49	221
Feburary	104	175
March	26	343
April	13	361
May	457	16
June	497	0
July	504	0
August	591	0
September	606	0
October	455	0
November	439	6
December	426	0
	4167	1122

* "Lockages" means that the boats and barges must be elevated or lowered by the lock to continue on their way.
** "Straight Throughs" describes the condition of "open river" in which barges go over the top of the dam because the river has been elevated owing to heavy rains or snow.

Arrival Times

Boats may approach the dam from opposite directions, but the first come–first served rule still holds. The total number of boats processed by the dam is somewhat cyclical due to river conditions and seasonal characteristics of the industries receiving materials by water. These data, as given, do not follow a Poisson distribution, so it must be reexpressed with respect to another time period. A sampling of hourly boat arrivals resulted in a Poisson distribution that allowed the data from Table 3.1 to be utilized.

The data for May through December were used to find the mean arrival time because they better describe the use of the dam and its locks. Furthermore, these data were used as an approximation of the queues developing in the period January through April. The fact that the river is relatively slow in rising or falling means that the lockages occur in groups for January and April, and that the queues that form follow, somewhat, the patterns found during the months of heavy usage.

Service Times

Numerous studies were made to determine the service time since no records were available giving these data. Service time was found to be exponentially distributed with a mean servicing time of forty minutes.

With these data it is possible to solve for E_n (the expected number of boats in the system), E_w (the expected number of boats waiting service), and E_t (the expected time an approaching boat will wait for service). This information is extremely important both to the owners of the boat and to the U.S. Corps of Engineers. An exceptionally long waiting time represents for the owners lost opportunity of business and poor equipment utilization. Consider, also how these costs may compound as a boat travels through numerous dams from the embarkation to destination points. To the Corps of Engineers, waiting time increases river congestion because more boats are needed to move materials and there is a heavier concentration of boats around the dam.

Solution

Utilizing the data May through December, the lockages = 3975 boats. Total number of 24 hour days = 245, total hours = 5880. Thus:

Arrivals (boats/hr) $= \dfrac{3975}{5880} = 0.676$ (boats arriving for service per hour).

Lockage (Service Time) $= 40 \min$ or $60 \min/40 \min = 1.5$ (average number of boats serviced per hour).

Therefore:

$\lambda = 0.676/\text{hr}$

$\mu = 1.500/\text{hr}$

$P = 0.676/1.500 = 0.451$

$P < 1$ which satisfies the restriction that $\dfrac{\lambda}{\mu} < 1$

$E_n = \dfrac{\lambda}{\mu - \lambda} = \dfrac{0.676}{1.500 - 0.676} = 0.820$ boats (serviced plus waiting)

$$E_w = \frac{\lambda^2}{\mu(\mu - \lambda)} = \frac{0.457}{1.5(0.824)} = \frac{0.475}{1.2360} = 0.370 \quad \text{boats (waiting for service)}$$

$$E_t = \frac{E_w}{\lambda} = \frac{0.370}{0.676} = 0.547 \quad \text{hr (time boat can expect to wait before being serviced)}$$

Table 3.2

n	$P_n(t)$ *	$P(N > n) = \left(\frac{\lambda}{\mu}\right)^{n+1}$ **
0	$1 - \frac{\lambda}{\mu} = 0.549$	$0.451 = 0.451$
1	$P_0(t)(0.451)^1 = 0.248$	$(0.451)^2 = 0.203$
2***	$P_0(t)(0.451)^2 = 0.112$	$(0.451)^3 = 0.092$
3	$P_0(t)(0.451)^3 = 0.050$	$(0.451)^4 = 0.041$
4	$P_0(t)(0.451)^4 = 0.023$	$(0.451)^5 = 0.019$
5	$P_0(t)(0.451)^5 = 0.010$	$(0.451)^6 = 0.008$
6	$P_0(t)(0.451)^6 = 0.005$	$(0.451)^7 = 0.004$

   * $P_n(t)$ = A barge has the probability $P_0(t) = 0.549$ of being immediately processed, $P_1(t) = 0.248$ of being the only barge awaiting service, $P_2(t) = 0.112$ of being second in line, etc. (given the first come, first served discipline).

  ** $P(N > n) = (\lambda/\mu)^{n+1}$ shows the complement of the cumulative probabilities for $P_n(t)$. Thus, when $n = 0$, the $Pr(N > 0)$ indicates the probability that the line size will be greater than zero $= (1 - 0.549) = 0.451$, $Pr(N > 1)$, (greater than one) $= [1 - (0.549 + 0.248)] = 0.203$.

*** A boat captain could reason that the probabilities of exactly one boat's being processed, and one waiting, when he arrived at the dam equalled 0.112, but the probabilities that there would be more than two $P(N > 2) = 0.092$; with these odds he would have an exceptionally good chance of meeting his delivery date.

Table 3.2 gives the probabilities for various n's. When $n = 2$, $P_2(t) = 0.112$, and $P(N > 2) = 0.092$.

The differences between two successive $P(N > n)$ values is equal to the individual P_n.

Thus the probability that there will be exactly two units in the system is equal to: Pr (there is more than one unit in the system) minus Pr (there are more than two units in the system) or $P_2(t) = P(N > 1) - P(N > 2) = 0.112$. Mathematically this is expressed as $(1 - \lambda/\mu)(\lambda/\mu)^2 \equiv (\lambda/\mu)^2 - (\lambda/\mu)^3 = 0.112$. From the $P(N > n)$ column in Table 3.2 it is seen that, for 9% of the time, more than two boats are waiting for service. If this is acceptable both to the owners and to the Corps of Engineers, then the present system is sufficient.

Cost Analysis

One boat represents a cost to the owners of \$226/hr. Thus, if it passes through six dams in one day, the waiting cost will be:

$$\frac{6 \text{ trips}}{\text{day}} \times \frac{0.547 \text{ hrs}}{\text{trip}} \times \frac{\$226}{\text{hr}} = 6 \times E_t \times \$226 = 6 \times 0.547 \times \$226$$

$$= \$742 \quad \text{(cost of waiting per day)}$$

Conclusion

Knowledge of waiting time will unquestionably aid the engineer in future designing projects and will also draw attention to the present problems. If the current situation is causing too much congestion and lost time, the engineers may theoretically change the values of μ to find an output rate to relieve the problem. A change in μ would mean faster pumps, more crew at the lock, improved methods of reducing crew-servicing time, faster gates, etc. If these were not economical, then new dams or more locks could be recommended.

A forecast of river traffic for the next few years may show an anticipated forty percent traffic increase with much larger and faster boat-barge combinations. This certainly will affect λ, and again the engineers and boat owners may use theoretical figures to project their waiting times, thereby determining the most economical course to be followed.[12]

3.62 One Line–One Server (Finite Population)[13]

General Formulas

1. $P_n = \left(\dfrac{m}{n}\right)\left(\dfrac{\lambda}{\mu}\right)^n P_0$ for $0 \leq n \leq S$ [14]

2. $P_n = \dfrac{m!}{(m-n)!}\left(\dfrac{\lambda}{\mu}\right)^n P_0$ for $S \leq n \leq m$

3. $\dfrac{P^n}{P_0} = \dfrac{m}{(m-n)!}\left(\dfrac{\lambda}{\mu}\right)^n$ [15]

[12] Theoretical changes in λ, μ, and the queue discipline are quite often used in evaluating waiting-line problems. This allows the analyst to test his model synthetically, thus providing a strong method of evaluating the system designed. These changes may be substituted into the mathematical formulas for the elementary model, but testing of this type is usually reserved for simulation techniques and the computer, especially for the more complex problems.

[13] For a comprehensive explanation see William Feller, *Introduction to Probability Theory and Its Applications* (John Wiley & Sons, Inc., New York, 1965, pp. 411–421).

[14] Any $P_n(t)$ will be designated as P_n when dealing with a finite universe, since this helps to determine which concept is being applied.

[15] P_0 must be known in order to use Formula 1 or 2. From the fact that

$$\sum_{n=0}^{m} P_n = 1. \text{ it follows that } \left(\frac{1}{P_0}\sum_{n=0}^{m} P_n\right)P_0 = 1 \text{ therefore } P_0 = \frac{1}{\dfrac{1}{P_0}\displaystyle\sum_{n=0}^{m} P_n} = \frac{1}{\displaystyle\sum_{n=0}^{m}\dfrac{P_n}{P_0}}$$

The individual P_n/P_0 ratios are calculated from formulas 1 and 2, as shown in formula 3. Thus, the sum of these ratios divided into one will yield the value for P_0. Once P_0 is known, all individual values for P_n are found. In Table 4.3, $P_1 = P_0(P_1/P_0) = 0.57463$ $(0.5000) = 0.28732$, and $P_2 = 0.57463\ (0.18750) = 0.10774$. Intuitively, the column P_n/P_0 may be expressed as the ratio of probability between the various P_n, given the fact that

4. $P_0 = \dfrac{1}{\sum\limits_{n=0}^{m} \dfrac{P_n}{P_0}}$

5. $E_w = m - \dfrac{\lambda + \mu}{\lambda}(1 - P_0)$

6. $E_t = \dfrac{1}{\mu(1 - P_0)}(E_w) = \dfrac{1}{\mu}\left(\dfrac{m}{1 - P_0} - \dfrac{\lambda + \mu}{\lambda}\right)$

7. $E_n = E_w + (1 - P_0) = m - \dfrac{\mu}{\lambda}(1 - P_0)$

8. $E_\Psi = E_t + \dfrac{1}{\mu} = \dfrac{1}{\mu}\left(\dfrac{m}{1 - P_0} - \dfrac{\lambda + \mu}{\lambda} + 1\right)$

Restrictions: (a) First Come–First Served Discipline and

(b) $\dfrac{\lambda}{\mu} < 1$.

EXAMPLE 3.   Studies show that of four machines breakdowns occur at random, the average time between breakdowns being one hour, and that a repairman averages one-eighth of an hour to service the idled machine.[16]

Thus $\lambda = 1$, $\mu = 8$, $m = 4$, and $\lambda/\mu = \frac{1}{8} = 0.125$ (which satisfy the restriction of $\lambda/\mu < 1$). With this information, solve for $P_0, E_w, E_t, E_n,$ and E_Ψ.

The first step in the solution of this problem is to solve for P_0 and then to work this value into the formulas for E_w, E_t, E_n and E_Ψ. In this problem the universe is a small countable set, and the removal of one machine from production drastically changes the probabilities of another's being removed. Finite queuing formulas are thus used, since a strong dependency relationship has been established. If the universe had been two hundred machines, then the removal of one would not have drastically changed the probabilities of another's being removed, and infinite queuing formulas could have applied. Finite formulas are laborious, especially when large numbers are involved, and this is why analysts prefer working with infinite queuing formulas, whenever applicable.

Table 3.3 was developed using finite formulas and shows the five values for all P_n.

$$P_0\left(\dfrac{P_0}{P_0} + \dfrac{P_1}{P_0} + \dfrac{P_2}{P_0} + \ldots \dfrac{P_n}{P_0}\right) = 1$$

Thus all probabilities are expressed with respect to P_0, and the ratio of the individual terms of P_n/P_0 is the same as that of their P_n counterparts. In Fig. 4.3 the ratio of $(P_2/P_3) \equiv (P_2/P_0)/(P_3/P_0)$ which is $0.10774/0.02694 \equiv 0.18750/0.04688$ or $4 \equiv 4$, which could have been verified earlier by cancelling P_0 in the second member of the identity.

[16] In finite queuing models there is a dependency relationship between arrivals, and the Poisson probability law is not applicable. Thus, instead of classifying arrivals as an average for the universe, it is necessary to classify them as an average of a unit time period.

Table 3.3

$n = Number$ of Units in the System	Size of Queue	Ratio of Probability		$P_n \mid P_0$**
			$\dfrac{P_n}{P_0}$	P_n
0	0	$1(\tfrac{1}{8})^0 = 1.00000$		0.57463
1	0	$4(\tfrac{1}{8})^1 = 0.50000$		0.28732
2	1	$12(\tfrac{1}{8})^2 = 0.18750$		0.10774
3	2	$24(\tfrac{1}{8})^3 = 0.04688$		0.02694
4	3	$24(\tfrac{1}{8})^4 = 0.00586$		0.00337
		$\sum \dfrac{P_n}{P_0*} = 1.74024$		$\sum P_n = 1.00000$

$*\ P_0 = \dfrac{1}{\sum \dfrac{P_n}{P_0}} = \dfrac{1}{1.74024} = 0.57463$ (formula 4)

** With the vlaue of P_0 known, each P_n follows from either formula 1 or formula 2. The notation $Pr(P_n \mid P_0)$ is read: the probability of P_n, given P_0.

Table 3.3 gives the value of $P_0 = \dfrac{1}{1.74024} = 0.57463$

Thus:

$$E_w = m - \frac{\lambda + \mu}{\lambda}(1 - P_0) = 4 - 9(0.42537) = 4 - 3.82833$$

$$= 0.17167 \text{ (machines waiting for service)}$$

$$E_t = \frac{0.17167}{8(0.42537)} = \frac{0.17167}{3.40296}$$

$$= 0.05045 \text{ (hours machine waits before being serviced)}$$

$$E_n = 0.17167 + 0.42537$$

$$= 0.59704 \text{ (number of machines being serviced plus waiting)}$$

$$E_\Psi = 0.05045 + 0.12500 = 0.17545 \text{ (hours machine is idle)}$$

P_m = The probability that m machines are being serviced or demanding service can be found be using Erlang's Loss Formula.[17]

$$P_m = \left[1 + \frac{1}{1!}\left(\frac{\mu}{\lambda}\right)^1 + \frac{1}{2!}\left(\frac{\mu}{\lambda}\right)^2 + \ldots + \frac{1}{m!}\left(\frac{\mu}{\lambda}\right)^m \right]^{-1}$$

Individual terms of P_m can then be found as follows:

$$P_m = \left[1 + 8 + \frac{64}{2} + \frac{512}{6} + \frac{4096}{24} \right]^{-1} = [297]^{-1} = \frac{1}{297}$$

In the expansion for P_m each term represents a ratio of probability similar to that of Table 3.3. The second term, $(1/1!)(\mu/\lambda)^1 = 8$, is four times smaller than the third term, $(1/2!)(\mu/\lambda)^2 = \frac{64}{2} = 32$, and their ratio, $\frac{8}{32}$, is similar to

[17] Erlang's Loss formula, named for A. K. Erlang, whom engineers regard as the first to utilize stochastic process in the solution of waiting lines.

the ratio (0.04688/0.18750) from Table 3.3. There are five terms in the series for P_m. If each term is divided by the sum of the term, the expression then becomes, through mathematical manipulation, a finite probabilistic series. Thus by using the fact that the ratio between the probabilities is similar to those found previously, it is easily verified that the first, second, third, fourth, and fifth terms equal P_4, P_3, P_2, P_1, and P_0, respectively.

Thus,

$$P_m = P_4 = \frac{1}{297} = 0.00337, \quad P_{m-1} = P_3 = \frac{8}{297} = 0.02694,$$

$$P_{m-2} = P_2 = \frac{32}{297} = 0.10774, \quad P_{m-3} = P_1 = \frac{85.33333}{297} = 0.28732,$$

$$\text{and} \quad P_{m-m} = P_0 = \frac{170.66667}{297} = 0.57463.$$

Looking back at the expression for $P_m = [1 + 8 + 32 + 85.33333 + 170.66667]^{-1}$, it is seen that each term of the series represents the ordered numerators for the various P_n.[18]

Cost Analysis

With machine costs of \$15.00/hr, operator costs of \$3.00/hr, and repairman costs of \$4.00/hr, the breakdown costs are:

(Machine Idle Time Costs)

    + (Lost Productivity of Machine Operator) + (Service Costs)

= (Hours Machine Idle)(Machine Costs)

    + $\dfrac{\text{(Hours Machine Idle)(Operator Costs)}}{\text{Number of Machines}}$

    + (Service Time)(Repairman Costs)

= $E_\Psi(\$15.00) + \frac{1}{4}(E_\Psi)(\$3.00) + (E_\Psi - E_t)(\$4.00)$

= $(0.17545)(\$15.00) + \frac{1}{4}(0.17545)(\$3.00) + (0.125)(\$4.00)$

= \$3.26334 (average cost per breakdown).

3.63 One Line–Multiple Server (Infinite Population)

General Formulas

1. $P_0(t) = \left[\left\{ \sum_{n=0}^{S-1} \frac{1}{n!}\left(\frac{\lambda}{\mu}\right)^n \right\} + \left\{ \frac{1}{S!}\left(\frac{\lambda}{\mu}\right)^S \left(\frac{S\mu}{S\mu - \lambda}\right) \right\} \right]^{-1}$

2. $P_n(t) = \frac{1}{n!}\left(\frac{\lambda}{\mu}\right)^n P_0(t) \quad \text{for} \quad n < S$

---

[18] Some analysts recommend using the formula $P_{m-k} = (1/K!)(\mu/\lambda)^k P_m$ to determine the individual terms of the expansion where $k =$ the number of machines in operation. If $k = 3$, then $P_{m-3} = P_1 = (1/3!)(\frac{8}{1})^3(1/297) = (512/6)\cdot(1/297) = 0.28732$. Notice that in the previous development for P_m each of these values was found without introducing a new variable k and additional manipulation.

3. $P_n(t) = \dfrac{1}{S! \cdot S^{n-S}} \left(\dfrac{\lambda}{\mu}\right)^n P_0(t)$ for $n \geq S$

4. $E_w = \dfrac{\lambda\mu\left(\dfrac{\lambda}{\mu}\right)^S}{(S-1)!\,(S\mu-\lambda)^2} P_0(t)$

5. $E_t = \dfrac{\mu\left(\dfrac{\lambda}{\mu}\right)^S}{(S-1)!\,(S\mu-\lambda)^2} P_0(t) = \dfrac{E_w}{\lambda}$

6. $E_n = \dfrac{\lambda\mu\left(\dfrac{\lambda}{\mu}\right)^S}{(S-1)!\,(S\mu-\lambda)^2} P_0(t) + \dfrac{\lambda}{\mu} = E_w + \dfrac{\lambda}{\mu}$

7. $E_\Psi = \dfrac{\mu\left(\dfrac{\lambda}{\mu}\right)^S}{(S-1)!\,(S\mu-\lambda)^2} P_0(t) + \dfrac{1}{\mu} = E_t + \dfrac{1}{\mu}$

Restrictions: (a) First Come First–Served Discipline

(b) $P = \dfrac{\lambda}{S\mu} < 1$ or $\dfrac{\lambda}{\mu} < S$.

EXAMPLE 4:   Some customers are more agressive than others and often force their way to the front of the line for immediate service. This practice causes much dissatisfaction and even a loss of customers for a florist shop located in the center of a large metropolis. To overcome this problem, each customer is required to take a numbered card upon entering the store. Thus, each customer is serviced by one of five clerks on a first come–first served basis. One clerk can serve an average of eight of the expected fifteen customers arriving each hour. A study of arrival and service times show that they respectively follow a Poisson and exponential distribution where: $\lambda = 15$ arrivals per hour, $\mu = 8$ services per hour, and $S = 5$ servers. Thus $\lambda/S\mu = \frac{15}{40}$, which satisfies the restriction $(\lambda/S\mu) < 1$. Find E_w, E_t, E_n, and E_Ψ.

In the development of this problem the logical first step is to solve for P_0 as this value is found in all formulas. Notice that this formula is divided into two parts. The first is the development of the individual values for $n < S$ and the second for all values $n \geq S$. In the first part a line cannot form because combined output is greater than input.

$$P_0(t) = \left\{\left[\frac{1}{0!}\left(\frac{15}{8}\right)^0 + \frac{1}{1!}\left(\frac{15}{8}\right)^1 + \frac{1}{2!}\left(\frac{15}{8}\right)^2 + \frac{1}{3!}\left(\frac{15}{8}\right)^3 + \frac{1}{4!}\left(\frac{15}{8}\right)^4\right] + \left[\frac{1}{5!}\left(\frac{15}{8}\right)^5\left(\frac{40}{40-15}\right)\right]\right\}^{-1}$$

$$P_0(t) = \left[1 + \frac{15}{8} + \frac{225}{128} + \frac{3375}{3072} + \frac{50625}{98304} + \frac{759375}{3932160} \cdot \left(\frac{40}{25}\right)\right]^{-1}$$

$$P_0(t) = [1 + 1.875 + 1.758 + 1.099 + 0.515 + 0.193 \cdot (1.600)]^{-1}$$

$$P_0(t) = [6.556]^{-1} = 0.152$$

Thus a line does not form until $n > S$. Table 3.4 verifies this fact, since a queue develops at $n > 6$ when $S = 5$.

Table 3.4

n	Queue Length	Idle Stations	Number Being Serviced	P_n
0	0	5	0	0.152
1	0	4	1	0.285
2	0	3	2	0.267
3	0	2	3	0.167
4	0	1	4	0.078
5*	0	0	5	0.029**
6	1	0	5	0.011***
7	2	0	5	0.004
8	3	0	5	0.001
.	.	.	.	.
etc.	.	.	.	.

* When $n \geq S$, each successive $P_n(t)$ value may be found by multiplying the previous value by $\lambda/(S\mu)$. This helped in the swift development of Table 3.4, avoiding the repeated use of formula 3.

** $P_5(t) \rightarrow P_6(t) = P_5(t)\left(\dfrac{\lambda}{S\mu}\right) = 0.029\left(\dfrac{15}{40}\right) = 0.10875 = 0.011$

*** $P_6(t) \rightarrow P_7(t) = P_6(t)\left(\dfrac{\lambda}{S\mu}\right)$

Formulas 2 and 3 are a logical consequence stemming from the development of P_0. Using these formulas, values for the individual $P_n(t)$ may be found. In Table 3.4 these individual values are shown for $n = 0$ to $n = 8$. They were calculated as follows

$$P_1(t) = (1.875)(0.152) = 0.285 \qquad \text{for} \quad n < S$$

$$P_2(t) = (1.758)(0.152) = 0.267 \qquad\qquad n < S$$

$$P_7(t) = \frac{1}{5!\,5^2}\left(\frac{15}{8}\right)^7 P_0(t) = \frac{170{,}859{,}375}{(3000)(2{,}097{,}152)} = 0.004 \qquad n \geq S$$

Once P_0 is found, the values for E_w, E_t, E_n, E_Ψ are readily calculated. Thus the expected number in queue–length of waiting line not including those being serviced is:

$$E_w = \frac{\lambda\mu\left(\dfrac{\lambda}{\mu}\right)^S}{(S-1)!\,(S\mu - \lambda)^2}\, P_0(t) = \frac{(15)(8)(\frac{15}{8})^5}{4!\,(40-15)^2}$$

$$= \frac{120(\frac{759{,}375}{32{,}768})}{24(625)}(0.153) = \frac{2780.914}{15{,}000}(0.153) = (0.185)(0.153)$$

$E_w = 0.028$ (Average number of customers waiting for service)

The expected waiting time in line is:

$$E_t = \frac{E_w}{\lambda} = \frac{0.028}{15} = 0.002 \text{ hrs} \quad \text{(Average time customer waits in line)}$$

The expected number being serviced plus waiting is:

$$E_n = E_w + \frac{\lambda}{\mu} = 0.028 + 1.875$$

$$= 1.903 \quad \text{(Average number of customers in the shop)}$$

The expected time in the system is:

$$E_\Psi = E_t + \frac{1}{\mu} = 0.002 + \tfrac{1}{8} = 0.002 + 0.125$$

$$= 0.127 \text{ hrs} \quad \text{(Average time customer spends in shop)}$$

If these were the conditions at a bank, supermarket, or tool crib, it might be assumed the system was overdesigned. But if waiting has a high priority, as is found with obstetrical cases in a hospital, life boats aboard a troop ship, and landing points for astronauts, then overdesign is acceptable. It most assuredly depends on the utility of waiting, which in many cases cannot be measured only by a pecuniary value.

3.64 One Line–Multiple Server (Finite Population)

General Formulas

1. $P_n = \left(\dfrac{m}{n}\right)\left(\dfrac{\lambda}{\mu}\right)^n P_0$ for $0 \leq n \leq S$

2. $P_n = \dfrac{m!}{(m-n)!\,S!\,S^{n-S}}\left(\dfrac{\lambda}{\mu}\right)^n P_0 \qquad S \leq n \leq m$ [19]

   In a multiple server model, $S > 1$, and either formula one or two holds, based on the restrictions imposed. When $S \geq n$, all inputs to the system are receiving service and there will be zero waiting lines.

3. $E_w = \displaystyle\sum_{n=S+1}^{m} (n-S)P_n = P_{S+1} + 2P_{S+2} + 3P_{S+3} + \ldots + (m-S)P_m$

4. $E_n = \displaystyle\sum_{n=0}^{m} nP_n$ where $E_w \subset E_n$

5. The expected machines in operation is given by:

$$E_0 = m - \sum_{n=0}^{m} nP_n = m - E_n$$

(which is simply the total universe minus the expected value of the machines in queue or being serviced).[20]

6. The expected number of operators being utilized equals:[21]

$$E_S = E_n - E_w$$

---

[19] When $S = 1$ this formula is identical to Formula #2, Sec. 3.62.

[20] In Sec. 3.4 this is defined as the expected number of elements that have not departed a finite universe for service.

[21] This was described in the glossary as the expected number of elements receiving service.

7. $E_t = \dfrac{E_w}{\mu(E_S)} = \dfrac{1}{\mu(E_S)} \sum\limits_{n=S+1}^{m} (n - S)P_n$

8. $E_\Psi = E_t + \dfrac{1}{\mu}$

The fraction or expected percent of a designated unit time that one operator is utilized equals:[22]

$$E_e = \frac{1}{S}(E_n - E_w)$$

This fraction may also be shown as:

$$E_e = \sum_{n=S+1}^{m} P_n + \frac{1}{S} \sum_{n=0}^{S} nP_n$$

Restriction: (a) First Come–First Served Discipline

(b) $\dfrac{\lambda}{S\mu} < 1.$

EXAMPLE 5:   The Quality Control laboratory of a chemical company has ten Chromatographic Analyzers which are used to determine the composition of the plastic products they are manufacturing. Through this continual evaluation the company is able to maintain the rigorous quality standards demanded by its customers. Four chemists operate these analyzers; they take the sample delivered from production, inject it into the machine, evaluate the data, and advise production of their findings. Each analyzer stops automatically when the analysis is finished. The random length of time between tests is determined by how long it takes to fractionate a column of the various chemicals, and studies show that these analyzers have an average operating interval of 60 minutes. Once a test is completed the analyzer may be restarted with another product. A chemist will average one half hour of work before getting the machine recycled, and there is always a backlog of work which, in some cases, proves exceptionally costly to the company. From this information it is found that $\lambda = 1$, $\mu = 2$, $m = 10$, $S = 4$, $\lambda/\mu = \frac{1}{2}$, and $\lambda/S\mu = \frac{1}{8}$ (which satisfy the restrictions that $\lambda/S\mu < 1$). Find E_w, E_0, E_n, E_S, and E_e.

Again, the first step in the solution of this problem is to solve for P_0. In this problem three new terms are introduced. They are paritcularly important owing to very high costs associated with equipment, possible production time lost while waiting for test results, and extremely high labor costs.

Table 3.5 shows the development of P_0 and other P_n. From these data, solution for the other terms follows by substitution. These formulas are left in their basic form because they reduce computational work, especially when much of the data are available directly from Table 3.5.

[22] Also defined as the expected utilization of S.

Table 3.5

n	Queue	$\dfrac{P_n}{P_0}$	P_n
0	0	1	$0.01517 = P_0$
1	0	5	0.07584
2	0	$\frac{45}{4}$	0.17065
3	0	$\frac{120}{8}$	0.22753
4	0	$\frac{210}{16}$	0.19909
5	1	$\frac{315}{32}$	0.14932
6	2	$\frac{1575}{256}$	0.09332
7	3	$\frac{1575}{512}$	0.04666
8	4	$\frac{4725}{4096}$	0.01750
9	5	$\frac{4725}{16,384}$	0.00437
10	6	$\frac{4725}{131,072}$	0.00055
		$\sum \dfrac{P_n}{P_0} = 65.92526$	1.00000

Thus:

$$E_w = \sum_{n=S+1}^{m} (n - S)P_n = P_{S+1} + 2P_{S+2} + 3P_{S+3} + \ldots + (m - S)P_m$$

$$= P_5 + 2P_6 + 3P_7 + \ldots + 6P_{10} = 0.14932 + 2(0.09332)$$

$$+ \; 3(0.04666) + 4(0.01750) + 5(0.00437) + 6(0.00055)$$

$$= 0.57109 \quad \text{(Expected number of analyzers not being used because}$$
$$\text{a chemist is not available to restart them).}$$

Notice that this formula for E_w is simply the sum of the individual queue sizes times their respective probabilities.

$$E_0 = m - \sum_{n=0}^{m} nP_n = 10 - [0P_0 + 1P_1 + 2P_2 + \ldots + 10P_{10}]$$

$$= 10 - [0 + 0.07584 + 2(0.17065) + 3(0.22753)$$

$$+ \ldots + 10(0.00055)] = 10 - 3.71406$$

$$= 6.28594 \quad \text{(Expected number of machines in operation)}$$

$$E_n = \sum_{n=0}^{m} nP_n = 3.71406 \quad \text{(Expected number of machines waiting or}$$
$$\text{being recycled)}$$

$$E_S = E_n - E_w = 3.71406 - 0.57109$$

$$= 3.14297 \quad \text{(Expected number of chemists being utilized)}$$

$$E_e = \frac{1}{S}(E_n - E_w) = \frac{3.71406 - 0.57109}{4} = 0.78574$$

$$= 78.6\% \quad \text{(Expected percent of day that a chemist is working)}$$

This may also be calculated as:

$$E_e = \sum_{n=S+1}^{m} P_n + \frac{1}{S} \sum_{n=0}^{S} nP_n = 0.31172 + 0.47410 = 0.78582 = 78.6\%$$

$$E_t = \frac{E_w}{\mu(E_S)} = \frac{0.57109}{2(3.14297)} = 0.09085 \text{ hr}$$

$$E_\Psi = E_w + \frac{1}{\mu} = 0.09085 + 0.500000 = 0.59085 \text{ hr}$$

Cost Analysis

Assume that these chemists have an annual salary of $12,480, one analyzer has a machine cost of $4 per hour, and a delay to production will cost $2000 per hour.[23] The daily lost-time costs are: (Analyzer Idle Time Costs) + (Lost Productivity of Chemist) + Recycling Costs = (E_Ψ) ($4.00/hr) + $(1 - E_e)$($6.00/hr) + $(E_\Psi - E_t)$($6.00/hr) = $6.64896/hr.[24]

3.65 Poisson Arrivals and Constant Service Times[25]

Mathematicians have shown that in the event of constant service times, the values found by traditional formulations are reduced by one half. Therefore, for a single line, single server case with Poisson Arrivals and constant service times, the following holds:

$$E_w = \tfrac{1}{2}E_w$$
$$E_n = \tfrac{1}{2}E_n$$
$$E_t = \tfrac{1}{2}E_t$$

EXAMPLE 6:   If the time to service one boat in Sec. 3.61, Example 2, were constant, then

[23] In the actual model, most testing was done in process, with other samples being transported to the quality-control laboratory by pneumatic tubes. The first come–first served discipline did not hold because samples were processed on a priority basis; but even the non-priority samples could cause a major delay if their slack time were expended. The solution to this problem required simulating a station-to-station priority queuing model. Before going into the costs of an expensive study, the second phase of the station-to-station model was quickly and cheaply approximated by algebraic formulae to determine whether this would justify further study.

[24] This figure is exclusive of costs associated with production delays.

[25] See Maurice Sasieni, Arthur Yaspan, Lawrence Friedman, *Operations Research: Methods and Problems* (New York: John Wiley & Sons, Inc., 1959) pp. 143–46, for more information about Erlang Service Times of which constant service is a special case.

In their book, the authors point out that: "The exponential assumption for service times gives only a one-parameter family (the parameter is μ) of possible service time distributions. This assumption is found to be unduly restrictive, partly because the exponential distribution has the property that larger service times are inherently less probable than smaller service times. A two parameter generalization of the exponential family, called the *Erlang* family of service time distributions, is highly useful in waiting line applications."

$$E_n = \tfrac{1}{2}(0.820) = 0.410 \text{ boats}$$
$$E_w = \tfrac{1}{2}(0.370) = 0.185 \text{ boats}$$
$$E_t = \tfrac{1}{2}(0.547) = 0.274 \text{ hours}$$

3.66 A Cost-Minimizing Model

Case History

In Example 2, Sec. 3.61, queues of boats were studied as they developed at one Ohio River Dam. To evaluate this problem a boat was estimated to cost the owners $226 per hour, but this was exclusive of barge costs and losses associated with the products carried.[26] Frequently one boat will push eight barges, with each containing 22,000 barrels of gasoline, fuel oils, lubricants, jet fuel, asphalt, and other petrochemicals. This is equivalent to more than one hundred trains, each pulling one hundred tank cars. A delay of these barges while being processed through the dam is also costly, but this, like other complicating factors, was not included in the original presentation.

Oil companies are continually investigating population shifts, changes in socio-economic characteristics, and per capita usage of their products. The effects of these and other studies usually result in companies moving their facilities, updating the old, or installing new ones to meet changing demands. Economic justification studies preceding the installation of new and larger bulk-processing facilities are more dependent on population growth than on other factors. Thus new facilities are generally situated within easy trucking distance of the more densely populated areas, since this helps minimize the cost of transportation.

Consider that an oil company has decided to build an extremely large bulk plant within a census area of five and one-half million people, and that this facility will be supplied *exclusively* by river transportation. It is estimated by the sales division that twelve 22,000-barrel barges will be required each week to meet demands for petroleum products. Thus the facilities planning group must determine those characteristics that will render optimal returns on investment for this single bulk-processing plant. One characteristic under consideration is how much and what type of pumping equipment should be adopted.

A planning group of the facilities section is assigned this one facet of the overall problem. It compiles information which shows that individual barge

---

[26] Evaporation of gasoline varies jointly with time, heat, and other factors. The longer a barge is in the system, the greater the evaporation. Oil companies may expect high costs because of waiting times in passage through numerous dams. Most petrochemicals are transported by pipeline, with shorter distances covered by barges; however these shorter barge trips involve processing through many dams.

arrivals follow a Poisson distribution.[27] Service data, the pumping of petroleum products into tank farms, are also collected, and they closely follow the exponential distribution.[28] Thus a Poisson-exponential model is accepted as representing the input-output functions.[29]

Each barge carries its own pump for discharging its product at the bulk plant. The time to unload these 22,000-barrel barges is rounded off at ten, twelve, fourteen, and sixteen hours. This includes set-up, make-ready, and other times. The planning group can dictate that this new bulk plant shall only accept barges with one specified pumping capacity. But the higher the capacity of the pump, the greater the cost at the tank-farm because higher-volume velocity pumps need larger lines, more expensive filtration equipment, greater heating capacity when pumping asphalt, and other expensive equipment. With higher pumping capacities, a higher facilities cost can be expected.[30] An idle barge costs money too, so this may be a compensating factor favoring increased capacity and the additional costs that accompany it. Instead of increasing the capacity of the pumps along with the matching facility, it may be wise to increase the number of stations and use lower capacity pumps. With more stations, barge waiting time could be reduced, but each barge would again require longer service times, and the additional facilities would require a larger capital investment.

Assume that there is space available for three unloading systems and that the facilities group has the authority to establish policy. From their studies they can adopt one of three systems and any of four type of pumps. Thus by the multiplication principle there are twelve possible ways from which to choose.

If the planning group determined that two stations, designed to accept fourteen hour capacity pumps, would minimize costs, it would follow that

[27] This new plant is the end of the line for each tow; a boat will have previously dropped off all but one barge at other bulk stations as it travels up river. After leaving the last barge, the boat will travel down stream, making a new tour of both cargo and empty barges. Previous studies indicated that a boat should not wait with barges, since this was too costly a procedure.

[28] Asphalt barges require much longer to set up as the product must be heated to improve flow rates. The pumping of this product requires substantially more time, but this analysis does not differentiate between service times for arriving barges. All service times are lumped into one distribution to simplify the model. This is often done in a real-world setting, for queuing theory does not distinguish between arrivals in an elementary analysis.

[29] Usually the collection of data only represents a sample of the total population. This is an acceptable practice if good statistical procedures are followed. Thus such things as sample size, representation, confidence intervals, and other statistical procedures should be considered.

[30] This facility will be located near the origin of the river, which is formed by two other smaller rivers. These larger barges and tows cannot navigate past this point. The population density is greater here, however, which means that planning for this facility will not include those plants situated upstream.

some other facilities downstream should also have stations that accept barges of this size; otherwise these barges would have only a single processing point, which would complicate scheduling. At the new plant, however, all stations will be identical; this too is for purposes of scheduling. For example, if the planning group wishes a μ_4 system, then all facilities will be designed with respect to this capacity.

Quantitatively to determine which system to use, the planning group gathers all information necessary to this problem and finds:

1. $\mu_1 = 16$, $\mu_2 = 14$, $\mu_3 = 12$, $\mu_4 = 10$ are the respective servicing station times for one barge;
2. $\mu_1 = \$72,270$, $\mu_2 = \$81,030$, $\mu_3 = \$94,170$, and $\mu_4 = \$11,169$ are the yearly fixed costs for the receiving facility;
3. $\mu_1 = \$39,420$, $\mu_2 = \$45,990$, $\mu_3 = \$56,940$, $\mu_4 = \$74,460$ are the yearly fixed costs per barge;
4. $\mu_1 = \$89,970$, $\mu_2 = \$100,740$, $\mu_3 = \$113,880$, $\mu_4 = \$137,970$ are the facilities' variable costs; and
5. $\mu_1 = \$111,690$, $\mu_2 = \$111,690$, $\mu_3 = \$111,690$, $\mu_4 = \$111,690$.

These are the barge yearly variable costs.

In this problem facility-fixed costs are constant, while facility-variable costs occur only when a barge is in the system. In the total analysis there will be waiting-time cost to consider, which also varies by the servicing system. For example a μ_3 service system will require a larger pump on the barge when compared to a μ_2 system. This accounts for the varying fixed-cost charges per barge. Variable cost, however, is dependent on lost opportunity. This stems from the fact that a barge, while in the unloading system, is unavailable for other work. Thus the quicker it can be returned to operation, the more fuel it may deliver on a yearly basis. Keeping a barge idle represents a lost opportunity for the company; for example, hourly waiting-time costs are a combination of fixed cost and lost opportunity. Thus a μ_3 barge will cost:

$$\frac{\$56,940 + \$111,690}{\$8760} = \$19.25 \text{ per hour.}[31]$$

Waiting Time Calculations

Thus far the planning group has these data with respect to a single service station:

[31] A company usually invests more money in a piece of equipment to reduce variable costs. Some analysts would place this additional cost per barge in the fixed costs of the total system. In fact, this additional cost should be kept separate. Consider a company that is buying new machinery: the more expensive machinery has higher productivity rates and possibly fewer rejects. If a company makes a set profit for each item produced, then keeping a more expensive piece of machinery waiting will certainly have a higher hourly premium. In this boat-barge problem a decision must be made which is more important to the total system design—keeping a barge waiting for the facility, the facility waiting for the barge, or minimizing cost with respect to both.

$$\lambda = \frac{12 \text{ barges per week}}{7 \text{ days per week}} = 1.71428 \text{ barges arriving per day}$$
$$= 0.07143 \text{ barges arriving per hour}$$

$$\mu_1 = \frac{24 \text{ hours per day}}{16 \text{ hours to unload one barge}} = 1.50000 \text{ barges serviced in one day}$$
$$= 0.06250 \text{ barges serviced in one hour}$$

$$\mu_2 = \frac{24 \text{ hours per day}}{14 \text{ hours to unload one barge}} = 1.71428 \text{ barges serviced in one day}$$
$$= 0.07148 \text{ barges serviced in one hour}$$

$$\mu_3 = \frac{24 \text{ hours per day}}{12 \text{ hours to unload one barge}} = 2.0000 \text{ barges serviced in one day}$$
$$= 0.08333 \text{ barges serviced in one hour}$$

$$\mu_4 = \frac{24 \text{ hours per day}}{10 \text{ hours to unload one barge}} = 2.40000 \text{ barges serviced in one day}$$
$$= 0.10000 \text{ barges serviced in one hour}$$

With these data it is possible to develop additional information for use in the solution of the overall problem. Thus:

Expected Utilization of Servicing System

Number of Stations on Facility

		S_1	S_2	S_3
C a p a c i t y	μ_1	0	0.5714	0.3810
Pump of	μ_2	0	0.5000	0.3333
	μ_3	0.8572	0.4286	0.2857
	μ_4	0.7143	0.3572	0.2381

$$\mu_1 S_2 = E_e = \frac{1}{S(E_n - E_w)} = \frac{\lambda}{S\mu} = \frac{0.07143}{2(0.06250)} = 0.5714$$

This formula was described in Sec. 3.64 as the fraction one operator is utilized. In this problem it is described as the fraction of one hour that the facility is utilized. Since this is an infinite queuing problem, $E_e = \lambda/S\mu$. Remember that this does not apply to data originating from a finite population. The cells $\mu_1 S_1$, and $\mu_2 S_1$ are eliminated from the matrix as

$$\mu_1 S_1 = \frac{0.07143}{(1)(0.06250)} = 1.14, \quad \text{and} \quad \mu_2 S_1 = \frac{0.07143}{(1)(0.07143)} = 1$$

which violates the restriction that $\lambda/S\mu < 1$.

$E_\Psi = $ *Expected Time a Barge Spends In the System (hours)*

	S_1	S_2	S_3
μ_1	0	23.76	17.08
μ_2	0	18.66	14.64
μ_3	84.10	14.70	12.35
μ_4	35.04	11.46	10.17

$$\mu_3 S_2 = \frac{\mu \left(\frac{\lambda}{\mu}\right)^S}{(S-1)!(S\mu - \lambda)^2} P_0(t) + \frac{1}{\mu} = \frac{0.0833(0.7348)0.4000}{1!(0.00907)} + 12 = 14.70$$

To complete this matrix it was necessary to calculate each value of P_0 for use in the formula for each E_Ψ.

Cost Analysis

Facility-Fixed Cost per Hour (dollars)

		S_1	S_2	S_3
Capacity of Pump	μ_1	0	16.50	24.75
	μ_2	0	18.50	27.75
	μ_3	10.75	21.50	32.25
	μ_4	12.75	25.50	38.25

$\mu_1 S_2$ = Two stations with μ_1 capacity = $2(\$72.270/8760)$ = \$16.50 fixed cost per hr.

Operating Costs Per Hour (dollars)

1	S_1	S_2	S_3
μ_1	0	11.71	11.71
μ_2	0	11.50	11.50
μ_3	11.14	11.14	11.14
μ_4	11.25	11.25	11.25

$\mu_3 S_2$ = (Number of stations used)(Hourly variable cost per station)(Expected utilization of servicing system) = $2\left(\dfrac{\$113,880}{8760}\right)(0.4286)$ = \$11.14

Barge Waiting Cost Per Hour (dollars)

1	S_1	S_2	S_3
μ_1	0	29.28	21.05
μ_2	0	23.99	18.82
μ_3	115.64	20.21	16.98
μ_4	53.19	17.39	15.44

$\mu_4 S_3 = \lambda(E_\Psi)$(Fixed plus variable barge costs per hour)
$$= 0.07143(10.17)\left(\frac{\$74,460 + \$111,690}{8760}\right) = \$15.44$$

Total Cost (dollars)

	S_1	S_2	S_3
μ_1	0	57.49	57.51
μ_2	0	53.99	58.07
μ_3	137.53	52.85	60.37
μ_4	77.19	54.14	64.94

$\mu_3 S_2$ = (Facility-fixed cost per hour) + (Operating cost per hour) + (Barge waiting cost per hour) = \$21.50 + \$11.14 + \$20.21 = \$52.85

Conclusion[32]

The total cost matrix shows the hourly values for each of the ten possibilities. Since this is a cost-minimizing model, the facility planning group will

[32] An additional example of this type of problem may be found in Maurice Sasieni, Arthur Yaspan, Lawrence Friedman, *Operations Research Methods and Problems* (John Wiley and Sons, Inc., New York, 1957), pp. 139–43.

recommend that the new bulk-processing plant should have two stations to accept barges with μ_3 capacity pumps.

3.7 MATHEMATICAL DERIVATIONS

3.71 Poisson Distribution—A Mathematical Approach

The Poisson distribution is derived from the following basic assumptions and postulates:

(1) The probability of the occurence of a success or failure is constant.
(2) The probability of a success or failure is independent of what has previously happened.
(3) The probability of an occurence or a change during time interval Δt is approximately proportional to Δt, provided that Δt is small.
(4) The probability of more than one occurence or change during any small interval Δt is approximately zero when compared to the probability of a single change during that interval.[33]

From the assumptions and postulates given it is possible to derive the formula for the Poisson distribution. The most common interval with which we are concerned is that of time. Our objective therefore is to find the probability of the number of changes (n) that occur during an interval of width (t), i.e.,

$$P_n(t) = P \quad (n \text{ changes in the interval } t).$$

Now let us increase the time interval t by a very small amount which we will designate by Δt. What is the probability that there will be n changes (arrivals, defects, etc.) in this slightly larger interval $t + \Delta t$?

Figure 3.2

To answer this question it is necessary to break down the problem into several parts. What we ultimately wish to find in the probability of n changes during the interval illustrated in Fig. 3.2 (Interval $= t + \Delta t$).

First, we will consider the probability of n changes in the interval Δt. By definition we know that $P_n(t)$ represents the probability of n changes in interval t. If we let λ equal the average number of changes in a unit interval, then $\lambda \Delta t$ would be the probability of one or more changes during interval

---

[33]The term *change* or *occurrence* can take on a variety of meanings when used in the solution of problems: It could mean arrival of a person at a doctor's office, the breakdown of a piece of equipment, defects on the production line, or many other things.

Δt. Therefore $1 - \lambda \Delta t$ would be the probability of zero changes in the interval Δt. To summarize the above in symbolic terms:

$P(n$ changes in interval t and no changes in interval $\Delta t)$

$$= [P_n(t)][1 - \lambda \Delta t]$$

Secondly, we consider the probability of $n - 1$ changes in the interval t and one change in the interval Δt; again we are dealing with n changes in the interval $t + \Delta t$. $P_{n-1}(t)$ by definition represents the probability of $n - 1$ changes in the interval t, and $\lambda \Delta t$ is the probability of one or more changes in the interval Δt. Therefore summarizing the above we have P_{n-1} changes in the interval t and one change in

$$\Delta t = [P_{n-1}(t)][\lambda \Delta t]$$

According to #4 of our basic assumptions, the probability that more than one change may occur in the interval Δt is negligible, assuming that the interval Δt is very small. Thus the probability of n changes in the interval $t + \Delta t$ would be obtained by simply adding the two probabilities as previously derived.

$$P_n(t + \Delta t) = P_n(t)(1 - \lambda \Delta t) + P_{n-1}(t)(\lambda \Delta t)$$
$$= P_n(t) - \lambda \Delta t P_n(t) + \lambda \Delta t P_{n-1}(t) \tag{1}$$

$$P_n(t + \Delta t) - P_n(t) = \lambda \Delta t P_n(t) - \lambda \Delta t P_n(t) \tag{2}$$

$$\frac{P_n(t + \Delta t) - P_n(t)}{\Delta t} = \frac{\lambda \Delta t P_{n-1}(t)}{\Delta t} - \frac{\lambda \Delta t P_n(t)}{\Delta t} \tag{3}$$

Returning to our assumption that Δt is very small in the above equations, we will let Δt approach zero. In terms of calculus this has special meaning; when we let Δt approach zero, the result is the first derivative of $P_n(t)$ which we designate by $P'_n(t)$. Thus

$$P'_n(t) = \lambda P_{n-1}(t) - \lambda P_n(t) \tag{4}$$

If $n = 0$, i.e., no change in the interval $t + \Delta t$, the term $\lambda P_{n-1}(t)$ cannot exist, therefore

$$P'_0(t) = -\lambda P_0(t) \tag{5}$$

Equation (5) shows that the first derivative is equal to a constant (λ) times the function itself $P_0(t)$. This is a unique functional derivative called the exponential function. Combining this with the fact that the probability of zero changes in the interval zero is equal to one, since we are assured of the correctness, we conclude that $P_0(t)$ is an exponential function written as follows:

$$P_0(t) = e^{-\lambda t} \tag{6}$$

Graphically, this function is portrayed as follows:

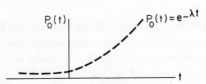

From the elementary algebra we know that $a^2 \cdot a^{-2} = 1$, or, applying this to our current problem, that $e^{-x} \cdot e^x = e^0 = 1$. Since the product of these two numbers is equal to one, this suggests the possibility of a probability distribution, because the summation of all terms in a probability distribution similarly equals one, i.e., $\sum p = 1$. Applying the series previously derived for e^x, and substituting this into the equation $e^{-x}e^x = 1$, we obtain the following:

$$1 = e^{-x}e^x = e^{-x}\left(1 + x + \frac{x^2}{2!} + \frac{x^3}{3!} + \frac{x^4}{4!} \cdots \frac{x^n}{n!}\right)$$

$$1 = e^{-x} + xe^{-x} + \frac{x^2e^{-x}}{2!} + \frac{x^3e^{-x}}{3!} + \frac{x^4e^{-x}}{4!} \cdots \frac{x^ne^{-x}}{n!} \tag{7}$$

Substituting λt for x we obtain the following distribution

$$1 = e^{-\lambda t} + \lambda te^{-\lambda t} + \frac{(\lambda t)^2e^{-\lambda t}}{2!} + \frac{(\lambda t)^3e^{-\lambda t}}{3!} + \ldots + \frac{(\lambda t)^ne^{-\lambda t}}{n!} \tag{8}$$

Each term of this distribution describes the probability of a specific number of events or arrivals during the period of time t. We also see that the first term $e^{-\lambda t}$ is exactly the same as the Equation (6), i.e., the probability of no events or arrivals during the time internal (t). Thus:

$$\frac{(\lambda t)^2e^{-\lambda t}}{2!}$$

would be the probability of exactly two events or arrivals during time interval t. By intuitive reasoning we conclude that

$$\frac{(\lambda t)^ne^{\lambda t}}{n!}$$

would be the probability of n events or arrivals during time interval t.

With the tools and concepts previously developed, the equations and formulas for a waiting line are readily derived. These formulas will be based on a special standard mathematical distribution—the Poisson distribution. Only if the arrivals and service rates are Poisson will the formulas apply.[34] If the arrivals are normal a stochastic process may be applied, but if the arrivals or service times represent some other nonlinear distribution, then either an entirely new set of mathematical models will have to be developed or it will be necessary to resort to simulation techniques.

[34]See John E. Freund, and Frank J. Williams, *Elementary Business Statistics— the Modern Approach* (Englewood Cliffs, N.J.: Prentice-Hall, Inc., 1964) pp. 410–15, for information covering the correspondence between a Poisson and exponential distribution.

We will first describe the Single Station Queuing Model with Poisson arrivals and Poisson service time. In this model there is only one service unit, and arrivals are serviced on a first come–first served basis. After the completion of this model, several additional models will be developed. The first will be derivations for a finite formula, while the second will develop the multiple server queuing model with Poisson arrivals and service rates.

3.72 One Line–One Server (Infinite Model)

What is the probability of exactly one unit entering the system and requesting service during the interval Δt? The Poisson formula developed earlier will permit us to relate the arrivals to the Poisson in the following manner

$$P_n(\Delta t) = \frac{(\lambda \, \Delta t)^n e^{-\lambda \, \Delta t}}{n!} \tag{9}$$

for $n = 1$

$$P_1(\Delta t) = (\lambda \, \Delta t)(e^{-\lambda \, \Delta t}) \tag{10}$$

When Δt becomes very small (approaches zero), $e^{-\lambda \, \Delta t}$ approaches one, as can be seen from the graph of the function. Therefore

$$P_1(\Delta t) = \lambda \, \Delta t \tag{11}$$

In order to simplify the derivation, we will make the assumption that the probability of more than one arrival or service requirement during Δt is so small that we can ignore this quantity. With this in mind, we can conclude that the probability of no units entering the system during Δt is $1 - \lambda \, \Delta t$. Similarly, the probability that no unit requires service during Δt is $1 - \mu \, \Delta t$.

With this information it is possible to write the probability of n units being in the system at time $t + \Delta t$.

$$\begin{aligned}
P_n(t + \Delta t) = &\; [P_n(t)(1 - \lambda \, \Delta t)(1 - \mu \, \Delta t)] \\
&+ [P_{n+1}(t)(1 - \lambda \, \Delta t)(\mu \, \Delta t)] \\
&+ [P_{n-1}(t)(\lambda \, \Delta t)(1 - \mu \, \Delta t)] \\
&+ [P_n(t)(\lambda \, \Delta t)(\mu \, \Delta t)]
\end{aligned} \tag{12}$$

Since we are assuming the probability of more than one arrival or service during Δt to be zero, these equations describe all possible situations which may occur. The first bracket is the probability of n units in the system at time t, multiplied by the probability of no arrivals during Δt multiplied by the probability of no servicing during Δt. The second is the probability of $n + 1$ units in the system at time t multiplied by the probability of no units entering the system during Δt, multiplied by the probability of one unit being serviced during Δt. The other brackets can be reasoned similarly.

Expanding and reorganizing Equation (12)

$$P_n(t + \Delta t) = P_n(t)[1 - \lambda\,\Delta t - \mu\,\Delta t + 2\mu\lambda(\Delta t)^2]$$
$$+ P_{n+1}(t)[\mu\,\Delta t - \mu\lambda(\Delta t)^2] \qquad (13)$$
$$+ P_{n-1}(t)[\lambda\,\Delta t - \mu\lambda(\Delta t)^2]$$

If we subtract $P_n(t)$ from both sides and divide by Δt, we obtain

$$\frac{P_n(t + \Delta t) - P_n(t)}{\Delta t} = \mu P_{n+1}(t) - (\lambda + \mu)P_n(t) + \lambda P_{n-1}(t)$$
$$+ \mu\lambda\,\Delta t[-P_{n+1}(t) + 2P_n(t) - P_{n-1}(t)] \qquad (14)$$

As Δt becomes closer and closer to zero, the last term of Equation (14) approaches zero. Similarly, as Δt approaches zero or becomes smaller and smaller, $P_n(t)$ and $P_n(t + \Delta t)$ will be equal, i.e., the probability of n arrivals in $P_n(t)$ is equal to the probability of n arrivals in $P_n(t + \Delta t)$. Therefore $P_n(t) - P_n(t + \Delta t) = 0$, thus

$$\mu P_{n+1}(t) - (\lambda + \mu)P_n(t) + \lambda P_{n-1}(t) = 0 \qquad (15)$$

Let us digress slightly now, and find the probability of zero arrivals during $t + \Delta t$, noting that $\lambda P_{-1}(t)$ is dropped because negative arrivals are impossible.

Using Equation (15) and seting $n = 0$, we obtain

$$\mu P_1(t) - (\lambda + \mu)P_0(t) = 0$$
$$\mu P_1(t) - \lambda P_0(t) - \mu P_0(t) = 0 \qquad (16)$$

However, $\mu P_0(t) = 0$ since an item cannot be serviced of there are zero items in service. Therefore

$$\mu P_1(t) - \lambda P_0(t) = 0$$
$$P_1(t) = \left(\frac{\lambda}{\mu}\right)P_0(t) \qquad (17)$$

Similarly, setting $n = 1$, we obtain

$$\mu P_2(t) - (\lambda + \mu)P_1(t) + \lambda P_0(t) = 0$$
$$\mu P_2(t) = (\lambda + \mu)\left(\frac{\lambda}{\mu}\right)P_0(t) - \lambda P_0(t)$$
$$P_2(t) = \left[(\lambda + \mu)\left(\frac{\lambda}{\mu}\right)\left(\frac{1}{\mu}\right) - \left(\frac{\lambda}{\mu}\right)\right]P_0(t) \qquad (18)$$
$$P_2(t) = \left(\frac{\lambda^2 + \lambda\mu - \lambda\mu}{\mu^2}\right)P_0(t)$$
$$P_2(t) = \left(\frac{\lambda^2}{\mu^2}\right)P_0(t) = \left(\frac{\lambda}{\mu}\right)^2 P_0(t)$$

If we set $n = 2$, we obtain

$$P_3(t) = \left(\frac{\lambda}{\mu}\right)^3 P_0(t) \qquad (19)$$

Continuing this procedure and using intuitive logic we find that

$$P_n(t) = \left(\frac{\lambda}{\mu}\right)^n P_0(t) \qquad (20)$$

We know from previous discussion that the sum of all terms in a probability distribution equals one, i.e.

$$\sum_{n=0}^{\infty} P_n(t) = 1 \qquad (21)$$

$$P_0(t) + P_0(t)\left(\frac{\lambda}{\mu}\right) + P_0(t)\left(\frac{\lambda}{\mu}\right)^2 + P_0(t)\left(\frac{\lambda}{\mu}\right)^3$$
$$+ \ldots + P_0(t)\left(\frac{\lambda}{\mu}\right)^n + \ldots = 1 \qquad (22)$$

$$P_0(t)\left[1 + \left(\frac{\lambda}{\mu}\right) + \left(\frac{\lambda}{\mu}\right)^2 + \ldots + \left(\frac{\lambda}{\mu}\right)^n + \ldots\right] = 1$$

This has now taken the form of a geometric progression of the following form:

$$1 + y + y^2 + y^3 + y^4 + \ldots + y^n + \ldots = \frac{1}{1-y} \qquad (23)$$

By letting $y = (\lambda/\mu)$; Equation (23) can be rewritten as $1/(1 - \lambda/\mu)$. Thus Equation (22) can also be re-expressed as:

$$P_0(t) = \frac{1}{1 - \left(\frac{\lambda}{\mu}\right)} = 1 \qquad (24)$$

and by dividing both sides of the equation by $1/(1 - \lambda/\mu)$:

$$P_0(t) = 1 - \frac{\lambda}{\mu} = \frac{\mu - \lambda}{\mu} \qquad (25)$$

This will give the probability of no units in the system when given the rate of arrival λ and the rate of service μ.

From Equation (20) we can compute the probability of $P_n(t)$ in terms of λ and μ by substitution:

$$P_n(t) = \left(\frac{\lambda}{\mu}\right)^n P_0(t) = \left(\frac{\lambda}{\mu}\right)^n\left(1 - \frac{\lambda}{\mu}\right) \qquad (26)$$

Expected value is a summations series defined as: (the probability of N_1 occuring) times (the value of N_1) or $[P_r(N_1)][N_1]$, plus (the probability of N_2 occuring) times (the value of N_2), etc. Algebraically this can be written as follows:

$$E(N) = P_1 N_1 + P_2 N_2 + P_3 N_3 + \ldots = \sum_{i=0}^{\infty} P_i N_i \qquad (27)$$

Applying this to our queuing model we can determine the expected number of units in the system, i.e the expected number in the waiting line and being serviced.

$$E_{(n)} = \sum_{n=0}^{\infty} P_n(t)(n) = \sum_{n=0}^{\infty} \left(1 - \frac{\lambda}{\mu}\right)\left(\frac{\lambda}{\mu}\right)^n(n)$$

By letting $(\lambda/\mu) = \rho$, the series now becomes

$$E_{(n)} = \sum_{n=0}^{\infty} n(1 - \rho)(\rho)^n = (1 - \rho)(\rho + 2\rho^2 + 3\rho^3 \ldots)$$

$$E_{(n)} = (1 - \rho)(\rho) \sum_{n=0}^{\infty} n\rho^{n-1}$$

Since

$$\sum_{K=0}^{\infty} Kb^{K-1} = \frac{1}{(1 - b)^2},$$

then

$$E_{(n)} = (1 - \rho)(\rho) \frac{1}{(1 - \rho)^2} = \frac{1}{1 - \rho} \quad \text{for} \quad \rho < 1 \qquad (28)$$

From Table 3.2, Sec. 3.61, Chapter 3, it may be verified that

$$E_n = \sum_{n=0}^{\infty} nP_n(t) \quad \text{and} \quad E_w = \sum_{n=2}^{\infty} (n - 1)P_n(t)$$

By the definition of these two terms,

$$E_w \subset E_n \quad \text{or} \quad E_w \to E_n$$

thus

$$\begin{aligned}
E_n - E_w &= [P_1(t) + 2P_2(t) + 3P_3(t) + 4P_4(t) + \ldots] \\
&\quad - [P_2(t) + 2P_3(t) + 3P_4(t) + \ldots] \\
&= [P_1(t) + P_2(t) + P_3(t) + P_4(t) + \ldots] = [1 - P_0(t)]
\end{aligned}$$

therefore

$$E_n - E_w = 1 - P_0(t) \quad \text{or} \quad E_w = E_n - (1 - P_0(t))$$

$$\begin{aligned}
E_w &= \frac{\lambda}{\mu - \lambda} - (1 - P_0(t)) \\
&= \frac{\lambda}{\mu - \lambda} - \left(1 - 1 + \frac{\lambda}{\mu}\right) = \frac{\lambda^2}{\mu(\mu - \lambda)}
\end{aligned} \qquad (29)$$

$(E_n - E_w)$ may also be described as the expected number being serviced, thus $E_S = (1 - P_0(t)) = (\lambda/\mu)$.

If μ represents the average number of services available in one time period, it is reasonable to assume that not all of these available services will be utilized, owing to the restriction that $(\lambda/\mu) < 1$. The average number of services in one time period, therefore, is dictated by λ, the average number of arrivals. So λ equals the average of arrivals per unit of time, but it also equals the average number of services per unit of time. The system is limited to service only those which arrive. Unused services cannot be inventoried. If $E_S = [1 - P_0(t)] =$ the expected number being serviced, and $\mu =$ the average capacity to serve in a unit time, then $\mu[1 - P_0(t)] =$ the average number serviced in a unit time. Intuitively, the algebraic identity of $\mu[1 - P_0(t)] = \lambda$ is thus proved. From this discussion the expected waiting time in line E_t may be developed.

A new arrival to the system expects to find a line size of E_w before him; therefore the time he must wait before service is the time required for clearing E_w. Thus

$$\frac{E_w}{\mu}[1 - P_0(t)] = \frac{E_w}{\lambda}$$

is the expected line size divided by the average number serviced in a unit time, which equals E_t, the expected time in the system.

$$E_t = \frac{E_w}{\lambda} = \frac{\lambda^2}{\mu(\mu - \lambda)} \cdot \frac{1}{\lambda} = \frac{\lambda}{\mu(\mu - \lambda)} \tag{30}$$

Note that λ and $\mu(1 - P_0(t))$ can be interchanged, but that this applies only to independent arrivals. In the case of finite queues where arrivals are not independent, $(E_w/\mu)(1 - P_0)$ is the proper expression for E_t.

If an element waits E_t before service, then the time in service is $1/\mu$. For example $\mu = 20$ services per hour; the service time for this one element is then $\frac{1}{20}$ hour. From this discussion it follows that the expected time an element spends in the system is $E_w + (1/\mu)$.

Therefore

$$E_\Psi = E_w + \frac{1}{\mu} = \frac{1}{\mu - \lambda} \tag{31}$$

3.73 One Line–One Server (Finite Model)

To convert the infinite equation to a finite model requires that the appropriate value for λ and μ be substituted into the previous development for $P_0(t + \Delta t)$ and $P_n(t + \Delta t)$. Thus from the general description that

$$P_0(t + \Delta t) = P_0(t + dt) = \mu P_1(t)\, dt + P_0(t)(1 - \lambda\, dt)$$

and

$$P_n(t + \Delta t) = P_n(t + dt)$$
$$= \mu P_{n+1}(t)\, dt + P_n(t)(1 - \lambda\, dt - \mu\, dt) + \lambda P_{n-1}(t)\, dt$$

the finite formula can be developed.

In the finite model, $m\lambda = \lambda_0$ is described as the condition where no elements have departed the universe of size m for service. With this constraint, $\mu_0 = 0$. Similarly, $(m - n)\lambda = \lambda_n$ is described as the condition where n elements have departed the universe of size m for service. From here, $\mu_n = \mu$. $P_0(t + dt)$ expressed in finite terms now becomes

$$P_0(t + dt) = \mu P_1(t)\, (dt) + P_0(t) - m\lambda P_0(t)\, dt$$
$$\frac{dP_n(t)}{dt} = \mu P_1(t) - m\lambda P_0(t)$$

By setting $[dP_n(t)/dt] = 0$, the conditions for equilibrium may be found thus:

$$P_1 = m\frac{\lambda}{\mu}P_0$$

continuing:

$$P_n(t + dt) = \mu P_{n+1}(t)\, dt + [1 - (m - n)\lambda\, dt + \mu\, dt]P_n(t)$$
$$+ (m - n + 1)\lambda P_{n-1}(t)\, dt$$
$$\frac{dP_n(t)}{dt} = \mu P_{n+1}(t) - [(m - n)\lambda + \mu]P_n(t) + (m - n + 1)\lambda P_{n-1}$$

Again,

$$\frac{dP_n(t)}{dt} = 0$$

for conditions of equilibrium

$$\mu P_{n+1} - [(m - n)\lambda + \mu]P_n + (m - n + 1)\lambda P_{n-1} = 0$$

Solving for $n = 1$,

$$\mu P_2 - [(m - 1)\lambda + \mu]P_1 + m\lambda P_0 = 0$$

$$\mu P_2 = [(m - 1)\lambda + \mu]\frac{m\lambda}{\mu}P_0 - m\lambda P_0$$

$$P_2 = [(m - 1)\lambda]\frac{m\lambda}{\mu^2}P_0 + m\frac{\lambda}{\mu}P_0 - \frac{m\lambda}{\mu}P_0$$

$$P_2 = m(m - 1)\frac{\lambda^2}{\mu^2}P_0$$

Continuing for successive values of n,

$$P_n = \frac{m!}{(m - n)!}\left(\frac{\lambda}{\mu}\right)^n P_0 \qquad 1 \leq n \leq m$$

and

$$P_n = \binom{m}{n}\left(\frac{\lambda}{\mu}\right)^n P_0 \qquad 0 \leq n \leq 1$$

From Table 3.3, Section 3.62, Chapter 3, it is verified that

$$E_n = \sum_{n=0}^{m} nP_n \quad \text{and} \quad E_w = \sum_{n=2}^{m} (n - 1)P_n$$

These are similar to the previously-developed values with the exception that they are limited by m, which represents the size of the supplying population. Thus, as found in previous developments:

$$E_s = (1 - P_0) \quad \text{and} \quad E_t = \frac{E_w}{\mu(1 - P_0)}$$

The number of elements that have not departed the finite universe for service E_0 may be described in one of two ways:

$$E_0 = m - E_n$$
$$E_0 = mP_0 + (m - 1)P_1 + (m - 2)P_2 + \ldots + (m - m)P_n$$

In sec. 3.74 the development of the Erlang Loss Formula is given with each term of the multinomial defined as either

$$P_n = \frac{1}{(m-n)!}\left(\frac{\mu}{\lambda}\right)^{m-n}P_m \quad \text{or} \quad P_{m-K} = \frac{1}{K!}\left(\frac{\mu}{\lambda}\right)^{K}P_m$$

Substituting this value into the equation for E_0 yields the expansion

$$\begin{aligned}
E_0 &= \frac{m}{m!}\left(\frac{\mu}{\lambda}\right)^{m}P_m + \frac{m-1}{(m-1)!}\left(\frac{\mu}{\lambda}\right)^{m-1}P_m \\
&\quad + \frac{m-2}{(m-2)!}\left(\frac{\mu}{\lambda}\right)^{m-2}P_m + \ldots + \frac{m-m}{(m-m)!}\left(\frac{\mu}{\lambda}\right)^{m-m}P_m \\
&= \frac{1}{(m-1)!}\left(\frac{\mu}{\lambda}\right)^{m}P_m + \frac{1}{(m-2)!}\left(\frac{\mu}{\lambda}\right)^{m-1}P_m \\
&\quad + \frac{1}{(m-3)!}\left(\frac{\mu}{\lambda}\right)^{m-2}P_m + \ldots + \left(\frac{\mu}{\lambda}\right)^{m-n}P_m \\
&= \frac{\mu}{\lambda}\left[\frac{1}{(m-1)!}\left(\frac{\mu}{\lambda}\right)^{m-1}P_m + \frac{1}{(m-2)!}\left(\frac{\mu}{\lambda}\right)^{m-2}P_m \right. \\
&\quad \left. + \frac{1}{(m-3)!}\left(\frac{\mu}{\lambda}\right)^{m-3}P_m + \ldots + P_m\right] \\
&= \frac{\mu}{\lambda}[P_1 + P_2 + P_3 + \ldots + P_m]
\end{aligned}$$

$$E_0 = \frac{\mu}{\lambda}[1 - P_0]$$

From the fact that $E_0 = m - E_n$ it follows that $E_n = m - E_0$. Thus by substitution

$$E_n = m - \frac{\mu}{\lambda}(1 - P_0)$$

Previously it was shown that $E_w = E_n - (1 - P_0)$. Therefore by substitution and clearing the equation,

$$E_w = m - \frac{\lambda + \mu}{\lambda}(1 - P_0)$$

Once this value is found, E_t and E_Ψ follow.

$$\begin{aligned}
E_t &= \frac{E_w}{\mu(1 - P_0)} = \frac{1}{\mu(1 - P_0)}\left[m - \frac{\lambda + \mu}{\lambda}(1 - P_0)\right] \\
&= \frac{1}{\mu}\left[\frac{m}{1 - P_0} - \frac{\lambda + \mu}{\lambda}\right]
\end{aligned}$$

$$E_\Psi = E_t + \frac{1}{\mu} = \frac{1}{\mu}\left(\frac{m}{1 - P_0} - \frac{\lambda + \mu}{\lambda} + 1\right)$$

It is important again to note that $\lambda \neq \mu(1 - P_0)$ in a finite development because of the dependency between arrivals.

3.74 Erlang Loss Formula

In Chapter 3; Table 3.3, it may be seen that the ratio of $P_4/P_0 = 28(\frac{1}{8})^4$. It therefore follows that

$$P_4 = 28(\tfrac{1}{8})^4 P_0$$

P_4 is defined in this model as the state in which all machines are in queue or being serviced. This is usually referred to as P_m where m represents the limit of the finite set.

In general form P_4 may be expressed as:

$$P_m = \frac{n!\binom{m}{n}\left(\dfrac{\lambda}{\mu}\right)^n}{\sum\limits_{n=0}^{m} n!\binom{m}{n}\left(\dfrac{\lambda}{\mu}\right)^n}$$

$$P_m = \frac{m!\left(\dfrac{\lambda}{\mu}\right)^m}{m!\left(\dfrac{\lambda}{\mu}\right)^m + (m-1)!\left(\dfrac{\lambda}{\mu}\right)^{m-1} + (m-2)!\left(\dfrac{\lambda}{\mu}\right)^{m-2} + (m-3)!\left(\dfrac{\lambda}{\mu}\right)^{m-3} + (m-4)!\left(\dfrac{\lambda}{\mu}\right)^{m-4}}$$

$$P_m = 1 + \left(\frac{\lambda}{\mu}\right) + 2!\left(\frac{\lambda}{\mu}\right)^2 + 3!\left(\frac{\lambda}{\mu}\right)^3 + 4!\left(\frac{\lambda}{\mu}\right)^4 + \ldots + m!\left(\frac{\lambda}{\mu}\right)^m$$

$$P_m = \left[1 + \frac{\mu}{\lambda} + \frac{1}{2!}\left(\frac{\mu}{\lambda}\right)^2 + \frac{1}{3!}\left(\frac{\mu}{\lambda}\right)^3 + \frac{1}{4!}\left(\frac{\mu}{\lambda}\right)^4 + \ldots + \frac{1}{m!}\left(\frac{\mu}{\lambda}\right)^m\right]^{-1}$$

From this general description any P_n may be found by the following:

$$P_n = \frac{1}{(m-n)!}\left(\frac{\mu}{\lambda}\right)^{m-n} P_m$$

or

$$P_{m-K} = \frac{1}{K!}\left(\frac{\mu}{\lambda}\right)^{K} P_m$$

where K equals the number of machines in operation.

3.75 One Line–Multiple Server (Infinite Population)

The previous derivations and explanations used only one service channel. If there are several service channels and one waiting line from an infinite population, a different set of equations can be developed. It will be assumed that the average service rate, μ, of each channel is the same. It was previously shown that the probability of a departure during Δt was denoted by $\mu \Delta t$. Letting n equal the number of elements in the system, and S equal the number of service channels, there are two variations of this waiting-line problem.

When the number of elements in the waiting line and in service are greater than the number of service channels $(n > S)$, the probability of a departure during Δt is then $S\mu \, \Delta t$. However if there are more channels than there are elements in the system, $(S > n)$, the probability of a departure is $n\mu \, \Delta t$. The following development will incorporate the assumption that $n > S$.

$$P_n(t + \Delta t) = P_n(t)(1 - \lambda \, \Delta t)(1 - S\mu \, \Delta t) + P_{n+1}(t)(S\mu \, \Delta t)(1 - \lambda \, \Delta t)$$
$$+ \; P_{n-1}(t)(\lambda \, \Delta t)(1 - S\mu \, \Delta t) + P_n(t)(\lambda \, \Delta t)(S\mu \, \Delta t) \ldots$$

Let $n = 0$; then $P_n(t + \Delta t) = P_0(t + \Delta t)$ where $P_{n-1}(t)$ is undefined

$$P_0(t + \Delta t) = P_0(t)(1 - \lambda \, \Delta t)(1 - S\mu \, \Delta t) + P_1(t)(S\mu \, \Delta t)(1 - \lambda \, \Delta t)$$
$$+ \; P_0(t)(\lambda \, \Delta t)(S\mu \, \Delta t)$$

$$P_0(t + \Delta t) = P_0(t) - P_0(t)(\lambda \, \Delta t) - P_0(t)S\mu \, \Delta t + P_0(t)S\mu\lambda(\Delta t)^2$$
$$+ \; P_1(t)(S\mu \, \Delta t) - P_1(t)S\mu\lambda(\Delta t)^2 + P_0(t)S\mu\lambda(\Delta t)^2$$

$$\frac{P_0(t + \Delta t) - P_0(t)}{\Delta t} = -\lambda P_0(t) - P_0(t)S\mu + P_1(t)S\mu = 0 \quad \text{as} \quad \Delta t \to 0$$
$$= -P_0(t)(\lambda + S\mu) + P_1(t)S\mu = 0$$

$$P_0(t)(\lambda + S\mu) = P_1(t)S\mu$$

$$P_1(t) = P_0(t)\left(1 + \frac{\lambda}{S\mu}\right)$$

From previous expansions and setting

$$\frac{dP_n(t)}{dt} = 0,$$

it is found that

$$-(\lambda + S\mu)P_n(t) + \lambda P_{n-1}(t) + S\mu P_{n+1}(t) = 0$$

Thus by transposing terms,

$$P_{n+1}(t) = \frac{\lambda}{S\mu} P_n(t) + P_n(t) + \frac{-\lambda}{S\mu} P_{n-1}(t)$$

Solving for $n = 1$,

$$P_2(t) = \frac{\lambda}{S\mu} P_1(t) + P_1(t) - \frac{\lambda}{S\mu} P_0(t)$$

Substitute

$$P_1(t) = P_0(t)\left(1 + \frac{\lambda}{S\mu}\right)$$

$$P_2(t) = \frac{\lambda}{S\mu}\left[1 + \frac{\lambda}{S\mu}\right] P_0(t) + \left[1 + \frac{\lambda}{S\mu}\right] P_0(t) - \frac{\lambda}{S\mu} P_0(t)$$

$$P_2(t) = \left(\frac{\lambda}{S\mu}\right)^2 P_0(t) + \left(\frac{\lambda}{S\mu}\right) P_0(t) + P_0(t)$$

$$P_2(t) = P_0(t)\left[\frac{\left(\dfrac{\lambda}{\mu}\right)^2}{S^2} + \frac{\left(\dfrac{\lambda}{\mu}\right)}{S} + 1\right]$$

Continuing for successive values of n, it is found that:

$$P_n(t) = P_0(t)\left[\frac{\left(\frac{\lambda}{\mu}\right)^n}{S^n} + \frac{\left(\frac{\lambda}{\mu}\right)^{n-1}}{S^{n-1}} + \ldots + 1\right]$$

which yields

$$P_n(t) = \frac{1}{S! \cdot S^{n-S}}\left(\frac{\lambda}{\mu}\right)^n P_0(t) \quad \text{for} \quad (n \geq S)$$

Utilizing the same procedure for the condition where $(S > n)$ and the probability of a departure is $n\mu \, \Delta t$, it may be readily formulated that

$$P_n(t) = \frac{1}{n!}\left(\frac{\lambda}{\mu}\right)^n P_0(t) \quad \text{for} \quad n < S$$

$P_n(t)$ is thus found by two separate and distinct equations. From these two distinct formulas for $P_n(t)$ where $n > S$ or $n < S$, the formula for $P_0(t)$ is readily derived. Consider the following table where $S = 4$.

Value of n	Size of Queue	P_n	Condition
0	0	$\frac{1}{0!}\left(\frac{\lambda}{\mu}\right)^0 P_0(t)$	$n < S$
1	0	$\frac{1}{1!}\left(\frac{\lambda}{\mu}\right)^1 P_0(t)$	$n < S$
2	0	$\frac{1}{2!}\left(\frac{\lambda}{\mu}\right)^2 P_0(t)$	$n < S$
3	0	$\frac{1}{3!}\left(\frac{\lambda}{\mu}\right)^3 P_0(t)$	$n < S$
4	0	$\frac{1}{4!} \cdot \frac{1}{4^0}\left(\frac{\lambda}{\mu}\right)^4 P_0(t)$	$n = S$
5	1	$\frac{1}{4!} \cdot \frac{1}{4^1}\left(\frac{\lambda}{\mu}\right)^5 P_0(t)$	$n > S$
6	2	$\frac{1}{4!} \cdot \frac{1}{4^2}\left(\frac{\lambda}{\mu}\right)^6 P_0(t)$	$n > S$
.	.	.	.
.	.	.	.
.	.	.	.

Given that $\sum_{n=0}^{\infty} P_n(t) = 1$, it therefore follows that:

$$P_0(t) + P_1(t) + P_2(t) + \ldots = 1$$

or

$$P_0(t) = \frac{1}{\sum_{n=1}^{S-1} P_n(t) + \sum_{n=S}^{\infty} P_n(t)}$$

From here it may be further developed that

$$P_n(t) = P_0(t)\left\{\left[\frac{1}{0!}\left(\frac{\lambda}{\mu}\right)^0 + \frac{1}{1!}\left(\frac{\lambda}{\mu}\right)^1 + \frac{1}{2!}\left(\frac{\lambda}{\mu}\right)^2 + \frac{1}{3!}\left(\frac{\lambda}{\mu}\right)^3\right]\right.$$

$$\left. + \left[\frac{1}{4!\,4^0}\left(\frac{\lambda}{\mu}\right)^4 + \frac{1}{4!\,4^1}\left(\frac{\lambda}{\mu}\right)^5 + \frac{1}{4!\,4^2}\left(\frac{\lambda}{\mu}\right)^6 \ldots\right]\right\}$$

$$P_n(t) = P_0(t)\left\{\left[\sum_{n=0}^{S-1}\frac{1}{n!}\left(\frac{\lambda}{\mu}\right)^n\right] + \frac{1}{4!\,4^0}\left(\frac{\lambda}{\mu}\right)^4\left[1 + \frac{1}{4}\left(\frac{\lambda}{\mu}\right) + \frac{1}{4^2}\left(\frac{\lambda}{\mu}\right)^2 \ldots\right]\right\}$$

Notice that the first set of values is found through the use of the equation for $P_n(t)$ when $n < S$. The second set, which pertains to the conditions where $n \geq S$, forms an infinite geometric progression after factoring. In this development, a (the first term) $= 1$, and r (the common ratio) $= \frac{1}{4}(\lambda/\mu)$.

$$P_n(t) = P_0(t)\left\{\left[\sum_{n=0}^{S-1}\frac{1}{n!}\left(\frac{\lambda}{\mu}\right)^n\right] + \frac{1}{4!\,4^0}\left(\frac{\lambda}{\mu}\right)^4\left[\lim_{n\to\infty} S_n = \frac{1}{1 - \frac{1}{4}(\lambda/\mu)}\right]\right\}$$

$$\lim_{n\to\infty} S_n = \frac{1}{1 - \frac{1}{4}(\lambda/\mu)} = \frac{4\mu}{4\mu - \lambda}$$

The second term of the expression P_n is now written in terms of S, which yields

$$\frac{1}{S!\,S^0}\left(\frac{\lambda}{\mu}\right)^S\left(\frac{S\mu}{S\mu - \lambda}\right)$$

therefore

$$P_n(t) = P_0(t)\left\{\left[\sum_{n=0}^{S-1}\frac{1}{n!}\left(\frac{\lambda}{\mu}\right)^n\right] + \left[\frac{1}{S!\,S^0}\left(\frac{\lambda}{\mu}\right)^S\left(\frac{S\mu}{S\mu - \lambda}\right)\right]\right\}$$

Given the $\sum_{n=0}^{\infty} P_n(t) = 1$, it follows that

$$P_0(t) = \frac{1}{\left\{\left[\sum_{n=0}^{S-1}\frac{1}{n!}\left(\frac{\lambda}{\mu}\right)^n\right] + \left[\frac{1}{S!}\left(\frac{\lambda}{\mu}\right)^S\left(\frac{S\mu}{S\mu - \lambda}\right)\right]\right\}}$$

By again referring to the development of this model, it can be seen that

$$E_w = \sum_{n=S+1}^{\infty} (n - S)P_n(t)$$

Referring to the previous expansions of P_n, the series for E_w begins when $n = 5$. This yields the following:

$$E_w = \sum_{n=S-1}^{\infty} (n - S)P_n(t)$$

$$= P_0(t)\left[\frac{1}{4!}\cdot\frac{1}{4}\left(\frac{\lambda}{\mu}\right)^5 + 2\cdot\frac{1}{4!}\cdot\frac{1}{4^2}\left(\frac{\lambda}{\mu}\right)^6 + 3\cdot\frac{1}{4!}\cdot\frac{1}{4^3}\left(\frac{\lambda}{\mu}\right)^7 + \ldots\right]$$

$$= P_0(t)\left\{\frac{1}{4!}\cdot\frac{1}{4}\left(\frac{\lambda}{\mu}\right)^5\left[1 + 2\cdot\frac{1}{4}\left(\frac{\lambda}{\mu}\right) + 3\cdot\frac{1}{4^2}\left(\frac{\lambda}{\mu}\right)^2 + \ldots\right]\right\}$$

By letting $x = \frac{1}{4}(\lambda/\mu)$ or $\lambda/4\mu$,

$$E_w = P_0(t)\left\{\frac{1}{4!}\cdot\frac{1}{4}\left(\frac{\lambda}{\mu}\right)^5[1 + 2x + 3x^2 + 4x^3 + \ldots]\right\}$$

$$= P_0(t)\left\{\frac{1}{4!}\cdot\frac{1}{4}\left(\frac{\lambda}{\mu}\right)^5[(1 - x)^{-2}]\right\} \quad \text{for} \quad x^2 < 1$$

$$= \frac{1}{4!}\cdot\frac{1}{4}\left(\frac{\lambda}{\mu}\right)^5\left[1 - \frac{1}{4}\left(\frac{\lambda}{\mu}\right)\right]^{-2} P_0(t)$$

$$= \frac{1}{S!}\cdot\frac{1}{S}\left(\frac{\lambda}{\mu}\right)^{S+1}\left[\frac{S\mu - \lambda}{S\mu}\right]^{-2} P_0(t)$$

$$E_w = \frac{\lambda\mu\left(\frac{\lambda}{\mu}\right)^S}{(S-1)!\,(S\mu-\lambda)^2}P_0(t)$$

In the single line, single server derivations for infinite populations it was found that $E_s = [1 - P_0(t)] = \lambda/\mu$. This carries a stipulation, however, that $\lambda/\mu < 1$. Thus it follows that $[1 - P_0(t)] = [P_1(t) + P_2(t) + P_3(t) + \ldots]$ is also less than one. In single line, multiple server developments this restriction is given as: $(\lambda/S\mu) < 1$ or $\lambda/\mu < S$. This is the same restriction previously used except that in a single line, single server model $\lambda/\mu < S \leftrightarrow \lambda/\mu < 1$. For multiple server model, $[1 - P_0(t)] \neq \lambda/\mu$; but $E_s = \lambda/\mu$. Again it is noted that λ/μ may be readily used in infinite queuing formulas but cannot be used similarly in finite queuing models because of the dependency relationship between arrivals.

Consider an example where $S = 4$, then

$$E_s = E_n - E_w = \sum_{n=0}^{\infty} nP_n(t) - \sum_{n=S+1}^{\infty} (n-S)P_n(t)$$

$$= [P_1(t) + 2P_2(t) + 3P_3(t) + \ldots] - [1P_5(t) + 2P_6(t) + 3P_7(t) + \ldots]$$

$$= [P_1(t) + 2P_2(t) + 3P_3(t) + 4P_4(t) + 4P_5(t) + 4P_6(t) + 4P_7(t) + \ldots]$$

$$= \left[\sum_{n=0}^{S-1} nP_n(t) + S\sum_{n=S}^{\infty} P_n(t)\right]$$

$$= P_0(t)\left[\frac{1}{1!}\left(\frac{\lambda}{\mu}\right) + \frac{2}{2!}\left(\frac{\lambda}{\mu}\right)^2 + \frac{3}{3!}\left(\frac{\lambda}{\mu}\right)^3 + \frac{4}{4!\,4^0}\left(\frac{\lambda}{\mu}\right)^4\right.$$

$$\left. + \frac{4}{4!\,4}\left(\frac{\lambda}{\mu}\right)^5 + \frac{4}{4!\,4^2}\left(\frac{\lambda}{\mu}\right)^6 + \ldots\right]$$

$$= \frac{\lambda}{\mu}P_0(t)\left[1 + \frac{\lambda}{\mu} + \frac{1}{2!}\left(\frac{\lambda}{\mu}\right)^2 + \frac{1}{3!}\left(\frac{\lambda}{\mu}\right)^3 + \frac{1}{4!}\left(\frac{\lambda}{\mu}\right)^4\right.$$

$$\left. + \frac{1}{4!\,4}\left(\frac{\lambda}{\mu}\right)^5 + \frac{1}{4!\,4^2}\left(\frac{\lambda}{\mu}\right)^6 + \ldots\right]$$

$$= \frac{\lambda}{\mu}\left[\sum_{n=0}^{\infty} P_n(t)\right] = \frac{\lambda}{\mu}(1) = \frac{\lambda}{\mu}$$

From this development and from proofs previously presented in Sec. 3.72, E_t, E_n, and E_Ψ follow

$$E_n = E_w + E_s = E_w + \frac{\lambda}{\mu} = \frac{\lambda\mu\left(\frac{\lambda}{\mu}\right)^S}{(S-1)!\,(S\mu-\lambda)^2}P_0(t) + \frac{\lambda}{\mu}$$

Given that the $E_s = \lambda/\mu$, it follows that $\mu E_s =$ the average number of services in one time period. Thus by substitution, $\mu(\lambda/\mu) = \lambda$, which again shows that the average number of services is dictated by the average number of arrivals. Thus,

$$E_t = \frac{E_w}{\lambda} = \frac{\mu\left(\frac{\lambda}{\mu}\right)^S}{(S-1)!\,(S\mu-\lambda)^2}P_0(t)$$

$$E_\Psi = E_t + \frac{1}{\mu} = \frac{\mu\left(\frac{\lambda}{\mu}\right)^S}{(S-1)!\,(S\mu - \lambda)^2} P_0 + \frac{1}{\mu}$$

3.76 Using e^x in Multichannel Queuing Models

Referring to the development of P_0 where

$$P_0 = \left\{\left[\sum_{n=0}^{S-1} \frac{1}{n!}\left(\frac{\lambda}{\mu}\right)^n\right] + \left[\frac{1}{S!}\left(\frac{\lambda}{\mu}\right)^S\left(\frac{S\mu}{S\mu - \lambda}\right)\right]\right\}^{-1},$$

the first term of this expression is:

$$\frac{1}{0!}\left(\frac{\lambda}{\mu}\right)^0 + \frac{1}{1!}\left(\frac{\lambda}{\mu}\right)^1 + \frac{1}{2!}\left(\frac{\lambda}{\mu}\right)^2 + \cdots + \frac{1}{(S-1)!}\left(\frac{\lambda}{\mu}\right)^{S-1}$$

This is a common mathematical series of e^x, but caution must be used in this substitution since larger numbers require numerous terms before the series converge.

$$P_0 = \left\{[e^x] + \left[\frac{1}{S!}\left(\frac{\lambda}{\mu}\right)^S\left(\frac{S\mu}{S\mu - \lambda}\right)\right]\right\}^{-1}$$

For example, Table 4.5 of Sec. 4.8 gives the value for $\sum_{n=0}^{S-1} (1/n!)(\lambda/\mu)^n$ as 18,588.19 $e^x = 18034$ for $x = 9.80$, and $e^x = 18,958$ for $x = 9.85$, which closely approximates the actual value of 18,588.19 for $x = 9.83$. Checking additional values of S will show a loss in reliability of e^x as a first-term predictor for this particular problem. Consult most elementary calculus texts for methods of testing when e^x converges.

3.8 DISCUSSION AND REVIEW QUESTIONS

1. Find E_n, E_w, E_t for a single line, single server model when arrivals are Poisson and service is exponential, given that λ/μ equals $\frac{2}{3}$.

2. Would the problem involving the waiting-time cost for the boats being processed through a dam change appreciably if another variable, such as whether the barges were filled or empty, were given in the problem?

3. Determine the number of machines one operator can economically service if each machine requires service once in ten hours and it takes one hour to service one machine. Assume that the machine costs are $20 per hour and the labor costs $5 per hour including fringe benefits. Check your results graphically with the charts given in Chapter 2. See Sec. 2.53, Figs. 2.5 and 2.6. Do they correspond? Why?

4. How many pumps would you recommend that a service station have if customers arrive every three minutes and the average service time is five minutes. Assume that this service station is on a four-lane highway and services only cars coming in one direction.

5. If the average profit per sale in Problem 4 were $.50 and the labor cost were $1.50 per hour, would you stay in business? Why?

6. Management has decided to increase the number of machines in Problem 3 and it realizes that this will require additional operators. Calculate the economical relationship for two, three, and four operators. Which would you recommend: that one operator run x machines, two operators y machines, three operators z machines, etc.? Show your results in tabular form.

7. Constant service is a rarity. Find two examples of constant service time. Be sure to include all phases of the service function.

8. Solve all phases of Example 2, Sec. 3.61, when service is considered constant at $1.75 per hour.

9. A constant service-time distribution has a standard derivation of zero. Is there a point at which constant service time formulas are preferred even though μ can be determined?

10. A company's trucks arrive continuously at its servicing dock of five stations at an average rate of three per half hour. If each truck remains at each dock for an average of three hours, would it be wise to: install a new service dock at a cost of $15,000 per year; improve servicing methods with new equipment at a cost of $18,500 per year; do both; or leave the system as it is? Assume that the service time is exponential, arrivals are Poisson, and a truck cost is $15.00 per hour.

11. Laborers who work near extremely hot operations are given frequent relief because of the intense heat. Rather than delay the operation, companies choose to have additional help to "spell-off" the men during their work. Examples of this may be found in the glass industry when working with refractories, the steel industry, etc. Assume that a crew of ten men has asked for additional relief men. The foreman and crew have asked for additional help because they are unable to meet their incentive; they say that they are frequently short of ten men, upon which the incentive is based. As an analyst you find that a man must leave his position at an average of twice per hour, and that he rests for an average of ten minutes. If the work crew is incorrectly sized, the incentive will be too easy and the company will suffer losses. In contrast to this, if the crew is too small, the company will also lose because the men will deliberately slow down, since there is "nothing in it" for them.

How many relief men would you recommend?

12. Rework Example 2, Sec. 3.61, for varying λ, and graph the results on E_n, E_w, E_t, and E_Ψ.

13. Rework Example 3, Sec. 3.61, for varying λ, and graph the results of E_n, E_w, E_t, and E_Ψ.

14. Develop a $P(N > n)$ table for Example 3, Sec. 3.61, as shown in Table 3.2.

15. In the manufacture of pipe tobacco, one machine produces eight completed packages per minute, given that the machines are 100% utilized. These machines, however, are subject to randomly occurring down time due to mechanical failures and other delays. Consider also that a machine will be subjected to machine interference because one operator is assigned five machines. After the completed package departs the machine it may be rejected because it is over or under weight; or an inspector may reject it owing to package conditions. If this area has twenty such machines, it may be clearly seen that total productivity will vary around a mean value.

When the system was originally designed, three carton-packaging machines were required for the four machine groups. Today's newer machine can package 240 individual packages per minute into cartons. If an engineer is assigned the project of re-layout to incorporate the new machine, what is the expected minimum length of conveyor required for the queues of packages that will develop in front of the carton-packaging machine? Each package is four and one-half inches long by three inches wide, with package orientation by length.

Consider that the carton package machine is to accept packages for three fourths of a minute and be operative for one fourth of a minute.

Bar Chart of an Average Cycle

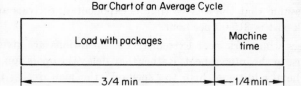

[See schematic representation of this problem on the next page.]

16. Given that $E_t = E_w/\lambda$ when

$$E_w = \frac{\lambda\mu\left(\dfrac{\lambda}{\mu}\right)^2}{(S-1)!\,(S\mu - \lambda)^2}\,P_0(t)$$

prove that:

$$\int_0^\infty t\,\frac{d[P(>t)]}{dt}\,dt = E_w + \frac{1}{\mu}$$

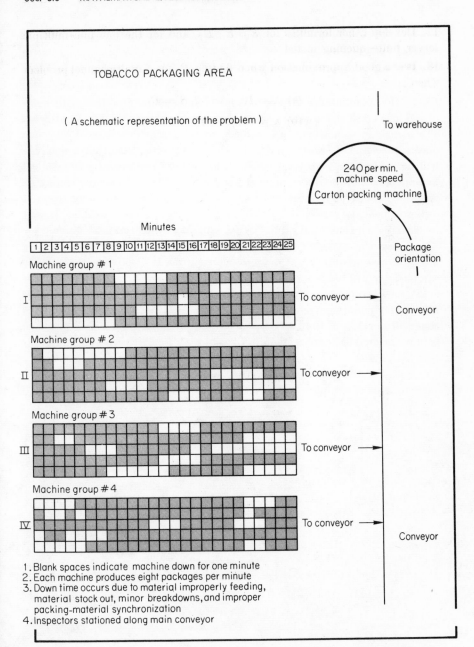

TOBACCO PACKAGING AREA

(A schematic representation of the problem)

To warehouse

240 per min.
machine speed

Carton packing machine

Minutes

| 1 | 2 | 3 | 4 | 5 | 6 | 7 | 8 | 9 | 10 | 11 | 12 | 13 | 14 | 15 | 16 | 17 | 18 | 19 | 20 | 21 | 22 | 23 | 24 | 25 |

Package
orientation

Machine group # 1

I   To conveyor ⟶   Conveyor

Machine group # 2

II   To conveyor ⟶

Machine group # 3

III   To conveyor ⟶

Machine group # 4

IV   To conveyor ⟶   Conveyor

1. Blank spaces indicate machine down for one minute
2. Each machine produces eight packages per minute
3. Down time occurs due to material improperly feeding,
   material stock out, minor breakdowns, and improper
   packing-material synchronization
4. Inspectors stationed along main conveyor

17. Develop other formulas for E_w, E_t, E_Ψ, and for the one line–multiple server finite queuing model.

18. Is e^x a good approximation when finding P_0 for a multichannel problem when

(a) $\lambda = 10, \mu = 2, S = 15$

(b) $\lambda = 5, \mu = 4\frac{3}{4},\ \ S = 8$

4 Case History :

The following case is introduced to improve understanding of queuing theory as applied to a real-life problem. Obviously, much is lost when only hypothetical situations are considered. The data and solutions gained from this mathematical exploration were actually used by the planning committee of Appalachia Memorial Hospital. Naturally, all information and analyses cannot be included, but some practical understanding of an actual model will result when the case is evaluated. Another reason for introducing a case history at this point is to broaden understanding of how waiting lines pervade most departments. The data presented throughout this case history will be used extensively in other chapters and review exercises. Therefore the reader should give considerable attention to all the enclosed quantitative materials.

This case introduces a number of queuing problems such as:

Admissions: (a) Planned arrivals–random service
Emergency: (b) Priority queues

Appalachia Memorial Hospital—

Including Mathematical Solution

Laboratory:	(c) Inefficient equipment utilization because of cyclical demand for service
Obstetrical:	(d) A classical case for: First come–First Served Discipline[1]
Surgery:	(e) Oversupplying needs due to decisions centering on uncertainty, which complicates scheduling.

---

[1] A bed is assigned whenever an obstetrical patient arrives at the hospital. The admission procedure is reversed, therefore, as the bed is first assigned and the patient located, her needs are satisfied and the admission data then gathered. Every patient, regardless of her condition, is assigned a bed unless there is none available. Lack of accommodations is studied in this case. There cannot be a priority bed assignment because the baby's delivery is an act generally without the control of man. Those with severe labor pains may deliver in ten hours while those experiencing little discomfort may deliver immediately. Thus for all situations an obstetrical bed assignment is made without respect to priorities and may therefore be characterized as a classical first come–first served queuing case.

4.1 INTRODUCTION: APPALACHIA
MEMORIAL HOSPITAL

The growth of hospitals in the United States has been phenomenal, and, as an employer, they rank fourth in the nation. However when cities are asked to rank their principal employers, it will be found that hospitals are named more frequently than others.

Appalachia Memorial Hospital is a 174-bed hospital servicing a small community in southeastern Ohio. It is a primary employer in the community and has undergone numerous expansions in its recent history.

Entering the hospital as a patient is an emotional experience, and anything not functioning perfectly is usually regarded with exaggerated concern. Patients are quick to voice their disapproval of food, personnel, services, and facilities. A five-minute delay to such persons seems an eternity, and they are quick to let everyone know it.

A hospital can be characterized as a whole series of waiting lines because every station in the complex has the potential of forming queues. With service being of utmost importance, and life and death often dependent upon the efficiency of the operations, the hospital is rather a good subject for consideration.

For the purposes of this case, only the areas of admissions, the emergency room, laboratory, obstetrics, and surgery will be evaluated.

4.2 ADMISSIONS: PLANNED ARRIVALS
AND RANDOM SERVICE

Hospitals have long been aware of the need to prevent queues from forming at the beginning—the Admission Office. Very often a doctor will call the hospital when a patient is to be admitted, giving the name of the patient, his accommodation preference, and a brief diagnosis, so that the admitting clerk will know in advance where to assign the anticipated patient. To hasten this process many hospitals have developed a very efficient mechanized system in this office whereby a single form, requiring only a few minutes for typing necessary information, such as name, address, doctor, type of financial arrangements, room preferences, is completed. This form is usually multi-paged so that a copy is available for each department to which the patient is assigned, i.e., the laboratory, pharmacy, X-ray, and record room, and business office.

Most hospitals have established a time that is best suited to admission, taking into consideration the patient's work-day schedule; any time from 8 AM to 4 PM is considered normal. Nevertheless there are times when queues form, regardless of all the precautions taken. When this occurs, complaints are often forthcoming. The administration may succumb to pressure and increase the admitting capacity, only to find that the utilization of the new facility or of personnel may be 15%, and even this increased capacity cannot guarantee that a waiting line, possibly smaller, will not form.

A precise time was allocated for admissions with a generous allotment of time for the processing of each patient; yet queues formed. An average time had been figured to process a patient, but in reality that average was seldom struck; the patient took either more or less time. If the time was less, there might not have been another patient available for immediate processing; if the time was longer, the next patient would have to wait. There is a probability of two, three, four, or more consecutive above-average processing times for patients which will stack the line awaiting service. Conversely, there may be service times less than average, but since arrivals are theoretically constant by virtue of planned admissions, the times savings cannot be banked (inventoried for future use) unless a line is already formed.

4.3 EMERGENCY ROOM: PRIORITY QUEUES

Appalachia Memorial Hospital has two emergency rooms with two stretchers (beds) in each room. One nurse is scheduled for each eight-hour shift to provide around-the-clock coverage for this department. There are no interns, which means that a family physician, or one that is available, will handle the emergency. Demand for emergency treatment is greater during the day and on weekends when doctors' offices are closed. Additional emergency personnel may be solicited from the nursing staff whenever extremely critical cases arrive. Sometimes servicing is performed on the ambulance stretcher.

Waiting lines easily form in the emergency area as arrivals (patients seeking treatment) and servicing time (time to treat an emergency) are difficult to predict for individual situations. Emergencies can be classified as major or minor, with major ones having priority for immediate service, which means that they go to the front of the line.

Queues form because of compounded probabilities. Tables 4.1 and 4.2 depict the actual situation.

Table 4.1

EMERGENCY ROOM
(Actual Data)

Daily Arrivals	Frequency	Total Patients	Probability
7	2	14	0.00548
8	0	0	
9	1	9	0.00274
10	4	40	0.01096
11	3	33	0.00822
12	9	108	0.02466
13	7	91	0.01918
14	15	210	0.04110
15	12	180	0.03288
16	27	432	0.07397
17	23	391	0.06301
18	22	396	0.06027
19	27	513	0.07397
20	28	560	0.07671
21	20	420	0.05479
22	22	484	0.06027
23	23	529	0.06301
24	19	456	0.05205
25	15	375	0.04110
26	12	312	0.03288
27	10	270	0.02740
28	19	532	0.05205
29	10	290	0.02740
30	5	150	0.01370
31	4	124	0.01096
32	6	192	0.01644
33	1	33	0.00274
34	3	102	0.00822
35	4	140	0.01096
36	2		
37	3	111	0.00822
38	1	38	0.00274
39	1	39	0.00274
40	1	40	0.00274
41	1	41	0.00274
.			
.			
.			
44	2	88	0.00548
.			
.			
.			
53	1	53	0.00274
	365	7868	1.00000

$$\text{Mean} = \frac{7868}{365} = 21.56$$

Table 4.2

EMERGENCY ROOM
(Actual Data)—12 Days of Information

Time in Minutes	Frequency	Total Minutes	Probability
0	2	0	0.00948
5	8	40	0.03791
10	29	290	0.13574
15	40	600	0.18957
20	22	440	0.10427
25	9	225	0.04265
30	32	960	0.15166
35	11	385	0.05213
40	16	640	0.07583
45	12	540	0.05687
50	3	150	0.01422
55	2	110	0.00948
60	8	480	0.03791
65	3	195	0.01422
70	2	140	0.00948
75	3	225	0.01422
80	3	240	0.01422
85	0		
90	3	270	0.01422
95	1	95	0.00474
100	0		
105	0		
110	1	110	0.00474
.			
.			
.			
.			
210	1	210	0.00474
	211	6345	1.00000

When the average arrivals per day are found for this sample, it calculates as: $\frac{211}{12} = 17.58$, which is slightly below the yearly mean for arrivals because twelve consecutive days is not representative of a whole year. Emergencies are actually seasonal. For example, intensity increases during the summer when young children are playing; pneumonia cases are greater during winter months. The mean calculates to be: $\frac{6345}{211} = 30.07$

4.4 LABORATORY: INEFFICIENT EQUIPMENT UTILIZATION

The laboratory consists of eighteen employees, each having a range of responsibilities that either duplicates or overlaps others. This is an essential feature since demands for certain laboratory analyses vary, which will result in considerable delay when a heavy demand for certain tests is the domain of only one specialist. Flexibility is essential for all personnel.

This department is similar to others in that it has priority jobs, e.g., typing the blood of a patient in emergency-room treatement. Priorities and an inability accurately to predict demand may destroy any attempt at scheduling and usually result in overstaffing.

Most work with a patient is performed during morning hours, which places a considerable strain on the laboratory. Some tests must receive immediate attention owing to degeneration of the sample. Laboratory technicians and assistants usually acquire these samples from the patient's room, which results in an irregular flow of work to the laboratory due to room and elevator queues. The situation is a compound one since incoming material from doctors' offices, sample degeneration, varying input, priority work, difficulty in predicting the total utilization of the house (hospital), and inability accurately to predict the demands for laboratory work as a function of the house size could result in large queues developing in the laboratory. The administration, cognizant of these problems but also aware of the wrath of patients, doctors, and family may choose to avoid any complications by overstaffing the needs.

This serves as a vital purpose however, as it satisfies the hospital board who, through lack of understanding, may measure the hospital's overall performance by how well "mother" was treated as a patient.

4.5 OBSTETRICAL: CLASSICAL CASE OF FIRST COME–FIRST SERVED DISCIPLINE

The obstetrical nursing station consists of twenty-two beds, three nurses, three aides, and one housekeeper, with the staff being reduced slightly during evening shifts. One nurse may be transferred out if demands do not warrant her presence, but she cannot be transferred back during that shift.

State regulation provides that one isolated section of the hospital be allocated for obstetrics. This is an outgrowth of past problems within cross-contamination. Some states have favorably altered this law during recent years.

The maintenance of a completely separate facility with a constant staff presents a difficult problem to the administration of a hospital. In an old hospital to allocate such a facility may result in an over- or underbed situation owing to the physical layout and changing needs. This can result

Table 4.3

OBSTETRICAL***
Deliveries, Abortions, Others (Actual Data)

	PATIENTS PER MONTH								CHI SQUARED TESTING	
Length of Stay	Actual Census				Total	Prob	Poisson Predictions with MEAN = 3.42*		Calculations	0.05 Level[†††] 7 Degrees of Freedom
Days	Jan	Jun	Sept	Oct	Total	Prob	Expected Total	Poisson Probability		
0[†]	3	2	2	4	11	0.038	10	0.033	$(10-11)^2/10 = 0.10$	
1	8	6	3	7	24	0.083	33	0.114	$(33-24)^2/33 = 2.45$	8 degrees
2	12	10	16	12	50	0.173	56	0.193	$(56-50)^2/56 = 0.64$	would be
3[††]	17	24	25	13	79	0.273	63	0.219	$(63-79)^2/63 = 4.06$	acceptable
4	15	16	12	13	56	0.194	54	0.186	$(54-56)^2/54 = 0.07$	according
5	10	10	7	10	37	0.128	36	0.126	$(36-37)^2/36 = 0.03$	to W. G.
6	6	1	3	7	17	0.059	21	0.072	$(21-17)^2/21 = 0.76$	Cochran[††††]
7	3	2	1	2	8	0.028	10	0.035	$(10-8)^2/10 = 0.40$	
8	1	1	1	1	4	0.014	4	0.015	$(4-4)^2/4 = 0$	
9	0	1	1	1	3	0.010	2	0.006	$(2-3)^2/2 = 0.50$	
	75	73	71	70	289	100	289	0.996	$= 9.01$	14.067

$$\frac{1}{n} \sum_{i=0}^{9} X_i f_i = \tfrac{1}{289}(0 + 24 + 100 + 237 + 224 + 185 + 102 + 56 + 32 + 27)$$

= Patient days/Patients = 987/289 = 3.42 average

* The Poisson prediction and Chi-squared values may be found in most handbooks of mathematical tables. See Sec. 4.10

** From Chi-squared charts

*** Actual data

† There is some error to the category of "Days 0," but it may be utilized for example purposes. Zero patient days is considered an admission for examination but no bed occupancy, which is somewhat vague.

†† In the chart for "Days 3," length of patient stay is not always determined by condition of patient. Doctor preference, financial situation, custom, demand for beds in the instance of a full house, etc. have a tendency to dictate the bed occupancy period. Fashionable doctors keep patients in hospitals an "acceptable" length of time, which shows that behavioralism influences many individual events that make up the probability distribution. This length of stay, however, is the service time that must be worked with regardless of reasons why.

††† The total calculated value of (9.01) is less than the chi-squared value of (14.067) for 7 degrees of freedom and a 5% significance level. Theoretically, it may be said with confidence that the Poisson distribution is a good fit. An analyst may ask these questions. Do input data come from a reliable source? What would be the case if Pr(zero days) = 0, or custom provides too much bias? Paraphrasing a national slogan, "THE DISTRIBUTION YOU SEE MAY BE YOUR OWN."

†††† Acheson J. Duncan, *Quality Control and Industrial Statistics* (Homewood, Ill.: Richard D. Irwin, Inc., 1956).

Table 4.4

OBSTETRICAL DEPARTMENT
(Actual Data)

Beds Being Used	Occurences	Patient Days**	Actual Probability	Poisson Probability Mean = 9.8†
0	0	0	0	0.0001
1	0	0	0	0.0005
2	1	2	0.0027	0.0027
3	1	3	0.0027	0.0087
4	4	16	0.0110	0.0213
5	18	90	0.0493	0.0418
6	28	168	0.0767	0.0682
7	27	189	0.0740	0.0955
8*	55 days	440	0.1507	0.1170
9	51	459	0.1397	0.1274
10	35	350	0.0959	0.1249
11	42	462	0.1151	0.1112
12	37	444	0.1014	0.0908††
13	19	247	0.0521	0.0685
14	15	210	0.0411	0.0479
15	18	270	0.0493***	0.0313
16	8	128	0.0219	0.0192
17	2	34	0.0055	0.0111
18	2	36	0.0055	0.0060
19	1	19	0.0027	0.0031
20	0	0	0.0000	0.0015
21	1	21	0.0027	0.0007
22	0	0	0.0000	0.0003
23	0	0	0.0000	0.0001
24	0	0	0.0000	0.0001
	365 Total	3588 Total	1.00	0.9999

* 55 days in a total of 365, 8 beds in 24 were being used
** 37 days, 12 beds were occupied which yields a total of $(37)(12) = 444$ patient days
*** $18/365 = 0.0493$
† From Poisson tables
†† Mean $= 3588/365 = 9.83$ patients or beds occupied

in excessive bed capacity (oversupplying needs) or rejection of obstetrical cases (undersupplying needs).[2]

The problem remains, then, that if a new facility (new hospital or extension of the present one) could be designed, how large should it have to be? Suppose that a mathematical study showed that a smaller facility would guarantee, ninety-five in one hundred trials, that the hospital would have enough capacity. It is doubtful whether the administration would approve

---

[2] Little condolence is found in either situation, but administrators generally oversupply to placate the patient or ease family emotions.

Figure 4.1

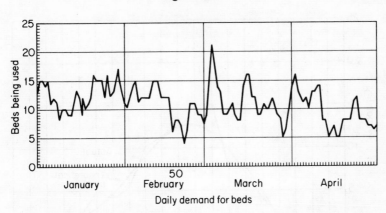

Daily demand for beds

a smaller structure, even with these figures, because historical records would show remote instances of heavier demand.

Appalachia Memorial Hospital has a twenty-two bed Obstetrical Unit. Tables 4.3 and 4.4 show utilization records for one year. Figure 4.1 shows that daily demand for beds fluctuates considerably, while Figs. 4.2 and 4.3 indicate

Figure 4.2

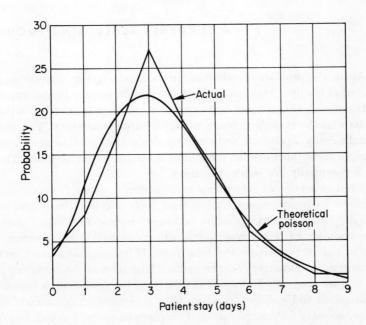

Figure 4.3

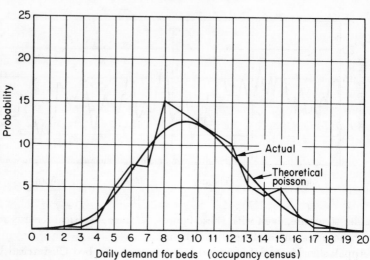

Daily demand for beds   (occupancy census)

that daily arrivals and length of stay follow a Poisson distribution. (*See Sec. 4.10 for information about the use of cumulative Poisson charts*).

4.6 SURGERY: SCHEDULING PROBLEMS

Again the problem of priorities arises as emergency operations go to the front of the line. At Appalachia Memorial four surgery rooms, two major and two minor, are provided by the hospital. From past records it is possible to determine the average times required for various operations. This includes the make-ready, operation, and clean-up times. Owing to the great variance in each of these functions the scheduling nurse overallocates times. Thus we have a potentially low room utilization.

Even this type of scheduling cannot stop a queue from developing; operations frequently require more than their allocated time, and this is especially true when an operation is "dirty" instead of "clean." Although make-ready time is fairly constant (easily predictable), the operation itself tends to reduce or increase the total time. If complications arise, or if for various reasons the surgery contaminates a large area of the operating room, the clean-up time will be longer. Similarly, if the operation is "clean" (no complications and spillage), clean-up time is reduced. A certain amount of time is necessary for resterilization. This plays havoc with scheduling, room utilization, staffing, and patient-family morale.

4.7 CONCLUSION

Statistical sampling studies conducted in numerous hospitals have shown many areas to be inefficient due to queues that develop. The underlying philosophy appears to be that of preparing for the worst situation. General duty nurses spend approximately five percent of their day with the patient, utilization of microscopes in the laboratory may be seven percent and obstetrical departments may be too large. The emotional consequences of what may happen if the hospital is not prepared in any situation certainly changes the utility value for space, equipment, and staff. When an individual has the opportunity of improving his holdings he measures the risks involved and acts according to his utility value for his present position. If one of these risks includes the possibility of losing everything, his decisions will certainly differ from what they would be were he to lose only a small part. Death of a company (bankruptcy) and death of an individual certainly change, at an accelerated rate, the risk-taking nature of the decision-maker.

In the past any attempt by a hospital administrator to reduce staff, space, and equipment may have been inappropriate when decisions were intuited. If a patient died because of inadequate staff, space, or equipment it was an impardonable sin, even if the possibility of this was one chance in a thousand; obviously, the way to prevent any recurrence was to have adequate staffing. The psychology of former administrators nurtured this philosophy, but in recent years, with the advent of sophisticated schools in hospital administration, decisions have become more objective. It has been found that services, space, equipment, and staff can all be better programmed with a minor outlay when the hospital is evaluated using mathematical techniques such as queuing theory.

4.8 MATHEMATICAL SOLUTION TO OBSTETRICAL CASE

A conflict arises in this case. Here the problem of utility value for money, services, and life all intertwine to emphasize that decision-making is not purely quantitative; but again, few could say after studying the facts of the case that a mathematical approach had not been enlightening.

To solve this problem it became necessary to evaluate what would happen to E_w, E_t, E_n, E_Ψ for the various values of s. Notice that E_n, E_Ψ approach the means previously found. In a multichannel queuing problem the laborious part involves solving for the P_0 value. This may be reduced, however, by utilizing the series e^x whenever applicable. Consider the problem, given single line, multiple server and first come–first served discipline,

where: $\lambda = 2.87$ patients arrive per day

$$\left(\frac{\text{Average Census}}{\text{Average Patient Stay}} = \frac{9.83}{3.42} = 2.87\right)$$

$\mu = 0.292$ patients served per each bed per day

$$\left(\frac{\text{One Bed Day}}{\text{Average Patient Stay}} = \frac{1}{3.42} = 0.292\right)$$

$S = 22$ number of beds (stations available)

$\dfrac{\lambda}{S\mu} < 1 =$ which satisfy the constraints of this problem

$\dfrac{\lambda}{\mu} = 2.87 \ (3.42) = 9.83$

$$P_0(t) = \left\{\left[\frac{1}{0!}\left(\frac{\lambda}{\mu}\right)^0 + \frac{1}{1!}\left(\frac{\lambda}{\mu}\right)^1 + \frac{1}{2!}\left(\frac{\lambda}{\mu}\right)^2 + \cdots \right.\right.$$
$$\left.\left. + \frac{1}{21!}\left(\frac{\lambda}{\mu}\right)^{21}\right] + \left[\frac{1}{22!}\left(\frac{\lambda}{\mu}\right)^{22}\left(\frac{6.424}{3.554}\right)\right]\right\}^{-1}$$

$$P_0(t) \approx \left[(e^x) + \frac{1}{22!}(9.8)^{22}\left(\frac{6.424}{3.554}\right)\right]$$

From the hospital administrator's viewpoint:[3]

$E_w =$ The number which must be placed in the hall or turned away.
$E_t =$ The expected time in the hall.
$E_n =$ The expected number in the hall or waiting, plus beds.
$E_\Psi =$ The expected time in the hall plus beds.

The objective function of this problem is to minimize E_w and E_t; but, the utility for these cannot be measured on cost alone—other factors must be considered. If the administrator wishes to gamble, he may choose a fourteen-bed department, but if he wishes to be safe he may settle for sixteen beds. Optimizing the decision purely through a numerical analysis may be somewhat unreliable, but a decision based solely on intuition is usually worse. If the administrator decides on a fourteen-bed department, the medical staff may disagree because they vividly remember days of greater demand. See Fig. 4.1, Sec. 4.5.

Choosing the proper-sized facility is extremely important to hospital planners due to rising costs and demands for better service. Any determination of the future size of the obstetrical department would be contingent on the anticipated growth of the population, change in the population's

---

[3] See Chapter 3, Sec. 3.76, for a more explicit description of e^x in queuing models.

socio-economic characteristics, and the currently diminishing per capita birth rate.[4]

Table 4.5 shows the logarithmic calculations for the various number of beds. To solve this problem, S (the number of beds) was altered, and

Table 4.5

SOLUTION OF OBSTETRICAL CASE

Through Use of Logarithms

S	$\log\left(\dfrac{\lambda}{\mu}\right)^S$	$\log S!$	$\dfrac{S\mu}{S\mu - \lambda}$	$\dfrac{1}{S!}\left(\dfrac{\lambda}{\mu}\right)^S$	$\sum \dfrac{1}{S!}\left(\dfrac{\lambda}{\mu}\right)^S$
0				1.00	1.00
1	0.9926	0.0000	$\dfrac{\lambda}{S\mu} > 1$	9.83	10.83
2	1.9852	0.3010	"	48.31	59.14
3	2.9778	0.7782	"	158.50	217.64
4	3.9704	1.3802	"	389.00	606.64
5	4.9630	2.0792	"	765.60	1372.24
6	5.9556	2.8573	"	1253.00	2625.24
7	6.9482	3.7024	"	1762.00	4387.24
8	7.9408	4.6055	"	2163.00	6550.24
9	8.9334	5.5598	"	2365.00	8915.24
10	9.9260	6.5598	58.40	2323.00	11239.24
11	10.9186	7.6012	9.39	2075.00	13314.24
12	11.9112	8.6803	5.53	1702.00	15016.24
13	12.9038	9.7943	4.10	1285.00	16301.24
14	13.8964	10.9404	3.36	903.60	17204.84
15	14.8890	12.1165	2.90	591.60	17796.44
16	15.8816	13.3206	2.59	363.90	18160.34
17	16.8742	14.5511	2.37	210.40	18370.74
18	17.8668	15.8063	2.20	115.10	18485.54
19	18.8594	17.0851	2.07	59.43	18545.27
20	19.8520	18.3861	1.97	29.24	18574.51
21	20.8446	19.7083	1.88	13.68	18588.19
22	21.8372	21.0508	1.81	6.11	18594.30

S	P_0	$(S\mu - \lambda)^2$	E_w	E_t	E_n	E_Ψ
10	$(144579.4)^{-1}$	.0025	53.9204	18.7859	63.7492	22.2106
11	$(\ 30723.9)^{-1}$	.1170	5.3294	1.8568	15.1582	5.2815
12	$(\ 22726.3)^{-1}$	.4020	1.8731	.6526	11.7019	4.0773
13	$(\ 20284.7)^{-1}$	.8575	.8051	.2805	10.6339	3.7052
14	$(\ 19337.3)^{-1}$	1.4835	.3695	.1287	10.1983	3.5534
15	$(\ 18920.5)^{-1}$	2.2801	.1705	.0594	9.9993	3.4841
16	$(\ 18738.9)^{-1}$	3.2472	.0795	.0277	9.9083	3.4524
17	$(\ 18658.9)^{-1}$	4.3848	.0364	.0127	9.8652	3.4374
18	$(\ 18624.0)^{-1}$	5.6930	.0162	.0056	9.8450	3.4303
19	$(\ 18608.9)^{-1}$	7.1717	.0077	.0027	9.8365	3.4274
20	$(\ 18602.9)^{-1}$	8.8209	.0029	.0010	9.8317	3.4257
21	$(\ 18500.2)^{-1}$	10.6406	.0012	.0004	9.8300	3.4251
22	$(\ 18599.3)^{-1}$	12.6309	.0005	.0002	9.8293	3.4249

[4] A diminishing birth rate will decrease λ, the daily per capita arrivals.

E_w, E_t, E_n, and E_Ψ were solved for each corresponding S. When $\lambda/(S\mu) > 1$, the original restrictions are violated. This is why no expected values are shown for S from 0–9. Notice that at $S = 10$, $\lambda/(S\mu)$ approaches one, which means that arrival rates approach the servicing capacity. This explains why E_w is so large for $S = 10$. Conversely, as the ratio $\lambda/(S\mu)$ approaches zero, E_w similarly gets smaller and also approaches zero. E_t and E_Ψ are not reliable measurements for this problem since it is inconceivable that waiting would result in a patient stay of 22.2106 days. This also holds, in part, for E_w and E_n. In this problem queuing theory is being used to establish S. Thus, if an S of sixteen beds were chosen, the administrator might reason that $E_w = $ (0.0795) patients would be in the hall only $E_t = 0.0277$ days, but that this would not increase E_w or E_Ψ. The obstetrical department would still only average 9.83 patients per day with a patient stay of 3.42 days because the physician would discharge the patient when she was well enough to go home. Thus, E_n and E_Ψ show that at $S = 16$ the system is approaching its λ/μ and μ values. In fact, these values do not change too drastically for values of $S \geq 13$. The ratio of S_{13} to S_{22} for both E_n and E_Ψ shows a change of only 8.19%. For safety the administrator would have chosen sixteen beds but, were he to gamble, he would choose $S = 14$, because E_n and E_Ψ are not *too far* from the actual means, and it *would be* possible to live with an average of 0.3695 patients in the hall for 0.1287 days.[5] If these figures were representative of a Diagnostic Clinic, E_w (patients waiting for admittance) E_t (days waiting to be admitted), E_n (total number of patients being diagnosed plus waiting for admittance), and E_Ψ (total elapsed time which includes waiting for admittance and time to complete tests) would all have easily detectable meaning.[6]

4.9 DISCUSSION AND REVIEW QUESTIONS

1. As administrator of Appalachia Memorial Hospital, how many beds would you plan to include in a new facility to house the Obstetrical Department? Why?

2. Develop probability graphs for the emergency room data Tables 4.1 and 4.2. Then graph a theoretical Poisson to compare each actual distribution subjectively.

3. Discuss how priority queues interrupt planning in the various departments of Appalachia Memorial Hospital.

[5] These are subjective evaluations which are governed by the administrator's utility value.

[6] Many times a patient must wait two, even three weeks before being accepted in many university-centered diagnostic clinics. Priorities take precedence, however, which means that the first come–first served discipline will not hold.

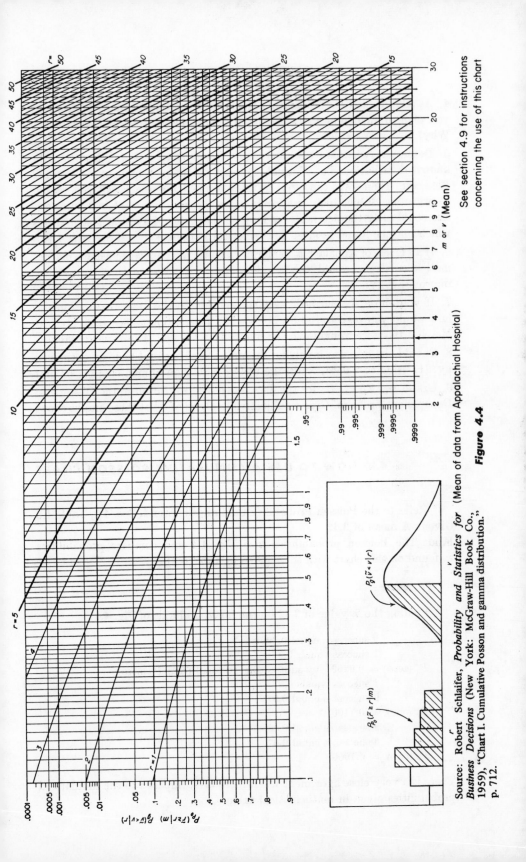

Figure 4.4

Source: Robert Schlaifer, *Probability and Statistics for Business Decisions* (New York: McGraw-Hill Book Co., 1959), "Chart I. Cumulative Posson and gamma distribution," p. 712.

(Mean of data from Appalachial Hospital)

See section 4.9 for instructions concerning the use of this chart

4. As administrator of Appalachia Memorial Hospital how many beds would you plan to include in a new facility to house the Obstetrical Department? Why?

5. Determine whether the Emergency Room Data follow a traditionally known distribution, i.e., Normal, Poisson, Negative Exponential, Gamma, Beta, etc. Then solve the problem using a queuing aproach, without regard to priorities. Subjectively analyze your results and then explain how priorities could alter the decisions made. (See the Table of Poisson distributions which may be found in most mathematical handbooks; also See Sec. 4.10).

6. If all facets of Appalachia Memorial Hospital were analyzed using a mathematical analysis, would the administrator's qualitative reasoning-ability improve? Why?

7. If you chose sixteen beds as your solution to the Obstetrical Problem, how would you placate those who said: "This solution is incorrect. Look at March 3,1965: we would have had five beds in the hall. This is inexcusable."

8. Should the decision involving the number of hospital beds be optimized by: (1) using cost data, or (2) the utility placed on human comfort or life?

9. Graph E_w, E_t, E_n, E_Ψ for the data given in the solution to the Obstetrical Department problem. Give a subjective analysis of what these graphs show.

4.10 HOW TO USE A CUMULATIVE POISSON CHART

Refer to the Poisson Probability Column, Chapter 4, Sec. 4.5, Table 4.3
Given: A mean of 3.42
Find: The Poisson probabilities (See Fig. 4.4 and compare probabilities as found on this chart with those given in Table 4.3)

Procedure:

Finding the m value of 3.42 on the horizontal axis of Fig. 4.4:

$$\begin{aligned}
&\text{0 successes equal 0.9999}\\
&\text{1 success equals 0.97}\\
P_r \text{ (zero)} &= 0.0299\text{—by subtracting } P_r \text{ (one) from } P_r \text{ (zero)}\\
&\text{1 success equals 0.97}\\
&\text{2 successes equal 0.87}\\
P_r \text{ (one)} &= 0.1100\\
&\text{2 successes equal 0.86}\\
&\text{3 successes equal 0.67}\\
P_r \text{ (two)} &= 0.1900
\end{aligned}$$

There is a very close agreement when these are compared to the tabularized probabilities given in mathematical tables.

5   Special Topics

5.1 PREFACE

Included in this chapter are problems that require a prior knowledge of elementary calculus, vectors and matrices, Markov chains, and computer programming. These are elementary examples, however, and with a little study they may be mastered even by those who lack formal training in these areas. Each section is footnoted so that those who wish additional information can immediately embark upon a self-study program. This chapter is divided into three separate problem areas: Sec. 5.2, Marketing Model (one line, one server; finite population); Sec. 5.3, A Servicing Problem (one line, one server; infinite population); Sec. 5.4, Markovian Queuing Models—a problem in equipment design, and a computer exercise. These examples are not all-inclusive but should prove thought-provoking. Thus, from their study, it will be recognized that waiting lines are a universal problem not restricted to a few specialized cases or disciplines.

in Mathematical Queuing Models

Marketing analysts have devoted considerable time to such topics as loyalty- and switching-characteristics of customers. If a sequence of marketing surveys yields the switching-characteristics of customers, then it is the analyst's problem to establish some predictability from these data. If a degree of predictability is established, then the decision parameter with respect to this specific problem will be reduced. Section 5.2 shows the effects of switching-characteristics in an exceptionally simplified marketing model.

Section 5.3 deals with customers balking at the size of the waiting line. The idea that potential customers balk at a long waiting time, or at any line whatever, has long been understood by retailers. The layout of a grocery supermarket is considered incorrect by some merchandizers if the entrance opens directly in front of check-outs because an improper first impression has been shown to restrict buying.

Section 5.4 shows an application of Markovian queuing processes to equipment design. For many years, plant layout, facilities planning, design, assembly line planning, etc, were solely in the hands of long-term employees who had experienced the problems. Thus, time was the primary teacher, with intuition a function of experience. Today it is possible to synthesize time through the power of mathematics, especially simulation processes, and so many younger men are working on problems formerly in the domain of others with more experience.

In the Markov queuing application, an engineer analytically solves a problem in design without having years of experience with the workings of the machine. Mathematics thus was proven an adequate substitute for intuition; actually, in most cases it is better, provided that care is taken in the original setup.

Also included in this section is an example of a computer solution to a mathematical queuing model. It is to be found in the discussion and review section because it is primarily a drill exercise in computer applications; it thereby differs from the other three examples, which deal both with a short case history and with the mathematical developments.

5.2 MARKETING MODEL[1] DETERMINATION OF BRAND SHARE

EXAMPLE 8:   An Elementary Model of Births and Deaths of Customers in a Finite Model. Assume that two products x and y command a finite market. From elementary marketing theory we know that a market saturates because of price, socio-economic characteristics of customer, geographical limitations of area, etc. Saturation may refer to two wholesale supply houses which competitively sell a specific item with limited demand.

Consider that farmers within a certain geographical area are serviced by one cooperative that sells two bulk tank cleaners—sanitizing agents. One contains iodine and the other chlorine. The market is limited by the number of dairy farms in the cooperative and the use of the state-approved sanitizers. Any loss of an iodine-user will result in a chlorine-user and vice versa. Thus the market is for most purposes bound.

Assume the market saturates at sixteen customers. From this it may be concluded that

$x =$ Iodine-user
$B_x =$ Births of new customers to iodine–death to a chlorine customer
$y =$ Chlorine-user

---

[1] See David W. Miller, Martin K. Starr, *Executive Decisions and Operations Research* (Englewood Cliffs, N.J.: Prentice-Hall, Inc., 1963), pp. 171–244, for a more comprehensive discussion of marketing models.

B_y = Birth of new customers to chlorine–death to an iodine customer $x \to y = x$ goes to y = a user of iodine switches brands and is now using chlorine.

If a market study shows the switching-characteristics to be: $x \to y = \frac{1}{3}$ (one to three) = for every iodine-customer who switches to chlorine three chlorine-customers switch to iodine, it follows that $y \to x = (3 \text{ to } 1)$ = for every three who switch to iodine one switches back to chlorine. This relationship holds because the market is finite and farmers must use one of these two state-approved products. This problem may be considered as a finite queuing problem, with respect to chlorine, where the arrivals $\lambda_c = 1$, and $\mu_c = 3$. If this problem had been worked with respect to iodine, then $\lambda_I/\mu_I = > 1$, thus violating the restrictions associated with previously given finite queuing formulas. Figure 5.1 depicts this model after many trials and where the system has reached a steady state.

Figure 5.1

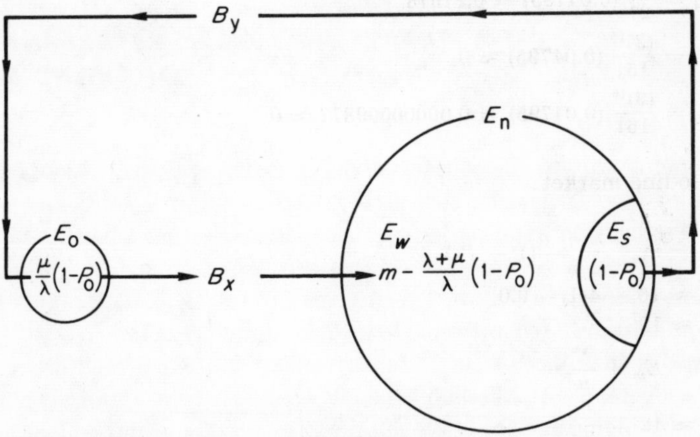

E_0 = Set of chlorine - users, E_n = Set of iodine users

E_w = Customers who have switched to iodine

E_s = Customers about to switch to chlorine but still using iodine

Notice that E_s is cleared from E_n, the market of iodine, at the rate of $1/[\mu_c(1 - p_0)] \approx \frac{1}{3}$, while the rate of a departure from E_0, the market size of chlorine, is $\lambda_c = 1$ by definition.

From these data it is possible to determine the market size commanded by each product. It is interesting to note that a market will reach a steady state and will remain split, as shown in Fig. 5.2, unless a trauma occurs, such as new state laws or allergies to one of the products.

Calculations for E_w, E_n, follow by using finite queuing formulas as given in Section 3.68. The first step is to solve for P_m and then for each P_n, given a one line, one server model and first come–first served discipline:

$$\frac{\mu_I}{\lambda_I} = \frac{\lambda_c}{\mu_c} = \frac{1}{3}$$

For every customer buying chlorine, three are departing the set to buy iodine.[2]

$$m = 16$$

Size of universe (number of farms supplied by one cooperative that use either iodine or chlorine sanitizer).

$$P_m = \left[1 + 3 + \frac{(3)^2}{2!} + \frac{(3)^3}{3!} + \ldots + \frac{(3)^{16}}{16!} \right]^{-1} = 20.855365^{-1}$$

$P_m = 0.04795$

$P_{16} = (1)\,(0.04795) = 0.04795$

$P_{15} = (3)\,(0.04795) = 0.14385$

$P_{14} = \dfrac{3^2}{2!}\,(0.04795) = 0.21578$

$P_1 = \dfrac{(3)^{15}}{15!}\,(0.04795) \approx 0$

$P_0 = \dfrac{(3)^{16}}{16!}\,(0.04795) = 0.00000009877 \approx 0$

Size of iodine market:

$$E_w = m - \frac{\lambda + \mu}{\lambda}(1 - P_0)$$

$E_w \approx 16 - 4(1 - 0.0)$

$E_w \approx 12$

$$E_n = E_w + \frac{\lambda}{\mu}$$

$E_n \approx 12 + \dfrac{1}{3}$

$E_n \approx 12.333$

Thus, by one interpretation, iodine commands

$$\frac{12.333}{16} \approx 77.1\% \text{ of the market.}$$

Another interpretation of the market is shown in Fig. 5.2 which displays the iodine market size for each P_n. The mode of this graph is approximately 13.5 customers. Remember that the size of the market is 100%, therefore

---

[2] This is the same as a finite queuing problem where the rate of arrivals $\lambda = 1$ and the service rate $\mu = 3$. Using these data and solving for E_n will yield the number in the system. This is the expected portion of the market that uses iodine sanitizers.

chlorine in this limited model commands the complement to each P_n of iodine. If there were more than two products, other queuing formulas would apply, but the total market would remain equal to one—provided that it is finite. This model is offered to show that queuing theory may improve the decision-maker's subjective evaluation of his marketing position; it is far from being all-inclusive.

Figure 5.2

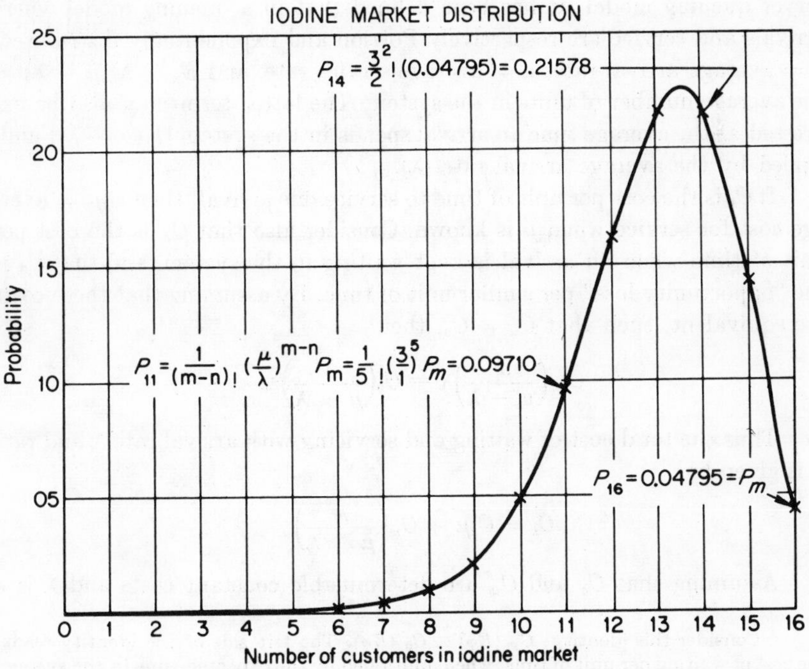
IODINE MARKET DISTRIBUTION
P14 = 3²/2! (0.04795) = 0.21578
P11 = 1/(m−n)! (μ/λ)^m−n Pm = 1/5! (3/1)^5 Pm = 0.09710
P16 = 0.04795 = Pm
Probability
25
20
15
10
05
0 1 2 3 4 5 6 7 8 9 10 11 12 13 14 15 16
Number of customers in iodine market

5.3 A SERVICING PROBLEM[3]

EXAMPLE 9: In queuing theory a servicing problem occurs when an approaching person observes the size of the line, anticipates a long wait, dislikes the composition of the line, and generally becomes by choice an isolate of the service system. An impatient customer is said to exercise judge-

[3] Inventory models may also be evaluated using queuing theory. See Horowitz, *An Introduction to Quantitative Business Analysis* (New York: McGraw-Hill Book Co., 1965), pp. 225–34.

ment, which from his frame of reference may be sufficient reason to choose another system for service. To a retailer this impatience could mean a loss of customers or decreased buying, but it may be classified by an electrical engineer as resistance. In the former instance this impatience is definitely undesirable, while in the latter it may be used advantageously. The utility values associated with an impatient person or element are not always measureable through cost analysis. For example, what dollar value should be assigned to the loss of a superior student because class enrollment is too large?

Consider a servicing problem as applied to the situation of a single server queuing model. It has been defined that in a queuing model where arrivals and service are respectively Poisson and exponentially distributed, λ = average arrival rate, μ = average service rate, and $E_n = \lambda/(\mu - \lambda)$ = the average number of units in the system. The latter term may also be expressed as the average time an arrival spends in the system $[1/(\mu - \lambda)]$ multiplied by the average arrival rate (λ).

If C_s is the cost per unit of time to service one arrival, then $C_s\mu$ = average cost for service when μ is known. Consider also that C_w is the cost per unit of time when an arrival is kept waiting in the system, and that C_0 is the "opportunity loss" per similar unit of time. By assuming that these costs are equivalent, such that $C_w = C_0$, then[4]

$$C_w\left(\frac{1}{\mu - \lambda}\right)\lambda \equiv C_0\left(\frac{1}{\mu - \lambda}\right)\lambda.$$

Thus the total cost of waiting and servicing with arrival rate λ and rate μ is given by[5]

$$C_t = C_s\mu + C_w\left(\frac{\lambda}{\mu - \lambda}\right)$$

Assuming that C_s and C_w are determinable constant costs and λ is a

[4] Consider this identity: $C_w(E_\Psi) \equiv C_0(E_\Psi)$. The left side of the identity reads: the cost of waiting per unit of time, when multiplied by the expected time in the system, yields the expected cost associated with losing the services of one operator, element, etc., while being processed through a servicing system. For example, if total labor cost is \$5.00 per hour, C_w, and the laborer spends a half-hour getting tools from a tool service system, E_Ψ, then the total cost would be $C_w(E_\Psi) = \$5.00(\frac{1}{2}) = \$2.50$. But this only represents one part of the company's loss. During this same period of time the laborer has not produced, and his machine has been idle. This, too, represents a loss to the company, and in this problem it is expressed as "opportunity loss." For example, assume that the company expects a profit of \$5.00 per hour from this one operator when he is working; the total cost to the company when the operator is not working is then similarly \$5.00 per hour. This is expressed in the right side of the identity as C_0. Thus, as in the previous example, the "opportunity loss" is calculated as $C_0(E_\Psi) = \$5.00(\frac{1}{2}) = \$2.50$. It must be noted that these two examples did not include the cost for performing the service-function, and so it is shown as a separate cost. In this example, $C_w = C_0$. Usually $C_0 > C_w$, because lost opportunity or idle facilities are greater than the labor rate of an idled employee.

[5] $C_t = C_s\mu + C_w[\lambda/(\mu - \lambda)]$ represents a total expected cost for an element that joins the system and waits until the service is terminated.

constant arrival rate, them μ becomes the controlling variable if total costs are to be minimized. It is known from calculus that given a functional relationship $C_t = f(\mu)$, then μ_0 is the critical value of μ. Thus the value of μ_0 obtained from solving $f'(\mu) = 0$ is a minimum when $f''(\mu) > 0$. Taking the first derivative of C_t with respect to μ:

$$\frac{dC_t}{d\mu} = f'(\mu) = C_s - \frac{C_w \lambda}{(\mu - \lambda)^2}$$

Setting

$$\frac{dC_t}{d\mu} = 0 = C_s - \frac{C_w \lambda}{(\mu - \lambda)^2}$$

to determine μ_0:

$$(\mu - \lambda)^2 = \frac{C_w}{C_s} \lambda$$

$$\mu - \lambda = \pm \sqrt{\frac{C_w}{C_s} \lambda}$$

If $\mu - \lambda$ equals a negative number, then $\lambda > \mu$; therefore $(\lambda/\mu) > 1$, which violates the restriction that $(\lambda/\mu) < 1$. Thus

$$\mu_0 = \lambda + \sqrt{\frac{C_w}{C_s} \lambda}$$

Taking the second derivative of $(t$ with respect to $\mu)$:

$$f''(\mu) = -C_w \left[\frac{-\lambda \cdot 2(\mu - \lambda)}{(\mu - \lambda)^4} \right] = \frac{2C_w \lambda}{(\mu - \lambda)^3}$$

Since one of the basic assumptions in our queuing model was that

$$\frac{\lambda}{\mu} < 1,$$

then

$$f''(\mu) = \frac{2C_w \lambda}{(\mu - \lambda)^3} > 0,$$

and

$$\mu_0 = \lambda + \sqrt{\frac{C_w}{C_s} \lambda}$$

is the minimum value in terms of the arrival rate plus the costs of servicing and waiting.

Case History

Many corporations have established new facilities along the Ohio River because of availability and cheapness of land, river transportation, abundance of water, electrical power, and in some cases preferential tax rates. These plants employ thousands of workers, some who reside on the opposite shore. Communities grow very rapidly with this industrial expansion as do the demands for local services. The river provides a natural barrier to intershore transportation and thus a bridge is constructed at a point midway between these vast industrial complexes. Originally, ferry boats were the only way to cross the river, at a cost of fifty cents per car. Now, either the free bridge or the ferry can be used. Since ferry boats operate almost on the door-step of the large plants, considerable time could be saved if this service were used; but the demand for this service is frequently so great that drivers will forego the ferry for the bridge and drive the additional thirty-two miles round trip. This avoids the cost of the ferry but results in the additional per-mile costs and a possible loss of time if the choice is ill-conceived. The boat owners recognize that a lost patron represents a lost opportunity for service and therefore consider expanding their facilities by adding a ferry.

Currently, cars arrive in a Poisson fashion at the rate of two cars every five minutes, and one ferry can service forty cars per hour. The owners anticipate, with another plant due to open, that potential services will increase. With better service their arrivals will grow from the current twenty-four to sixty cars per hour. Studies show that a loss of a customer causes their total cost for service to rise, $C_s = \$0.02$ per car for each car lost, and that lost profits, due to lost customers $= C_0 = C_w = \$0.12$ per car. Using the previously developed formulas that find the optimum service rate with respect to minimized costs, it is found that:[6]

$$\mu_0 = \lambda + \sqrt{\frac{C_w}{C_s}\lambda} = 24 + \sqrt{\frac{0.12}{0.02}}\, 24 = 24 + \sqrt{144}$$

$$\mu_0 = 36 \quad \text{cars per hour}$$

Owing to the manner in which shifts begin and end, the boat-owners anticipate only sixty cars from one side. Thus for cost analysis a ferry is considered to return empty to the demanding side.

A used ferry can be purchased for $10,000; with improved service each ferry will average thirty cars per hour. To determine if this is a profitable

---

[6] By letting $C_w = C_0$, the previously developed minimizing formula can be used, but now it is with respect to cost associated with lost opportunity rather than with respect to costs of servicing and waiting. This "opportunity loss" formula is $C_t = C_s\mu + C_0\lambda/\mu - \lambda$, which is also minimized with respect to μ by the formula

$$\mu_0 = \lambda + \sqrt{\frac{C_w}{C_s}\lambda} \equiv \lambda + \sqrt{\frac{C_0}{C_s}\lambda}$$

This formula now measures how to minimize loss due to customers going elsewhere, while previously the formula determined how to minimize costs. Interpreting this rather loosely, one could say that this was the way to minimize our loss for not having a waiting line. The same formula is used because C_s is given and $C_w = C_0$.

endeavor assume straight-line depreciation over ten years with twenty-four-hour operations every day. The cost is spread over 8760 hours per year. Thus depreciation costs for a new ferry are

$$C_h = \frac{1000}{8760} = \frac{\$0.114}{\text{hr}}$$

The cost per hour for two ferries is[7]

$$C_t' = C_s\mu' + C_w\left(\frac{\lambda}{\mu' - \lambda}\right) + C_h$$

$$= (0.02)(60) + (0.12)\left(\frac{24}{60 - 24}\right) + 0.114$$

$$C_t = 1.394$$

The cost per hour for a single ferry is

$$C_t = C_s\mu + C_w\left(\frac{\lambda}{\mu - \lambda}\right)$$

$$= (0.02)(36) + 0.12\left(\frac{24}{36 - 24}\right)$$

$$C_t = 0.96$$

Since $C_t' > C_t$, the owner should not buy a new ferry, when the decision is based on total cost only.

If service costs were eliminated from equations for C_t and C_t', then $C_t' \not> C_t$ and the new boat would be warranted. In such a case the owner would assume the increased service cost to decrease the waiting time for the customers.

Costs now are:

$$C_t' = 0.08 + 0.144 = 0.194$$

$$C_t = 0.240$$

Since $C_t' < C_t$, then the projected profit of the new boat can be substantiated.

5.4 MARKOVIAN QUEUING MODELS

5.41 Introduction

An interesting queuing problem develops when n is limited although arrivals emanate from an infinite source. Examples of these are:

[7] $\mu' = 2\mu = 60$ for two lines.

1. Announcements for laboring jobs at a hand glass company. The foreman limits the size of the line, and the rest are turned away. This still exists in industries today.
2. Lines are limited to the legal seating capacity at athletic events. The rest are turned away.
3. Special sales, offering the first hundred customers discount prices.

These may appear somewhat vague, but an industrial application should strengthen understanding.

5.42 Application to Industry

EXAMPLE 10:   A nailing machine drives four equally-spaced nails with one stroke. Each of the four driving heads must have a nail to drive because a missed one must be driven by hand at considerable expense. To minimize such occurrences each driving head is equipped with a storage tube that holds ten nails. These tubes are not hand-filled owing to cost. A hopper that holds 10,000 nails is filled at the beginning of the shift and the nails are delivered to the individual tubes by vibrators. If the tube is filled, the nail that is to enter is not admitted and the tube is by-passed. Each tube will have (10 − 1) = 9 nails at the conclusion of one successful stroke of four nails and thus may accept one nail from the hopper. Nails feed into the tubes only between strokes, so it is possible that some tubes will begin the next operation with only nine nails in storage because of a missed feed. If this were to continue, an individual tube would be out of nails in ten strokes, which would result in production delay. The nails cannot haphazardly fall into these tubes, so they must be presented point first. Rather than orient each individual nail, the machine's designers simply introduce an abundance of nails to an orientation slot before the tubes, knowing that the probabilities are high one will be delivered by the vibrators in the proper alignment. Thus, at the conclusion of two strokes, three of the feed slots may have nine nails while one has only eight owing to a missed feed. The object is to have the feed tube long enough so that, given a period of time, enough nails will present themselves to the slot, thereby filling the tube again and virtually guaranteeing that each head will have a nail to drive.

The length of a tube is very important in the design of the machine. A tube that is too large will result in a larger machine and may prove too cumbersome for production-line work. If shorter tubes are necessary to the design, the probability of correct alignment must be improved. This will increase the nail feed rate, thus allowing each tube to inventory fewer nails.

The nailing machine, when used on a production line, will not be utilized to its full capacity. Randomly-occurring machine breakdowns, a varying work pace, production delays from prior work stations, and other factors contribute to decreased machine efficiency. Thus service time, strokes per hour, are given in average instead of constant units.

From this abbreviated description it may be summarized that:

1. A nail is not admitted to the tube if the tube is full.
2. If the nail is not properly oriented it will not be admitted.
3. There is a probability that a second, third ... tenth stroke may be completed before a nail is presented to the tube due to orientation or jamming problems.[8]
4. Tube length must be held to a minimum because of machine design.
5. The feed tubes are closed during the driving procedure, so a properly oriented nail can only be admitted between strokes.
6. Service, the driving of a nail, occurs randomly as demand for an individual stroke is governed by material flow to the operator and his work pace.
7. A feed tube that inventories nails can be full, partially full, or empty. Thus:
   a. A full feed tube postively rejects since n is limited.
   b. An empty feed tube accepts between strokes provided that the nail is properly oriented.
   c. A partially-filled tube may decrease by one (machine strokes—the nail is not replaced), increase by one (no stroke—one replaced), stay the same (no stroke—none replaced).

Problem for Solution

An engineer is assigned the problem of redesigning the old machine. He finds that the machine can be substantially reduced in size if the feed tubes are shortened, the orientation device is improved, the hopper reduced, the delivery vibrator improved, etc.[9] He would like to have each head with a feed tube capacity of four.

In the set-up of the problem, the engineer assigns values to his problem so that:

$$\lambda = Pr \quad \text{(A nail feeds into the tube)} = \text{Nail's mean arrival rate expressed as a probability}$$

$$1 - \lambda = Pr \quad \text{(A nail does not feed into tube).}$$

$$\mu = Pr \quad \text{(Machine strokes, and nail departs tube)} = \text{Nail's mean departure rate expressed as a probability}$$

$$1 - \mu = Pr \quad \text{(Machine does not stroke—zero departures)}$$

$$\lambda(1 - \mu) = \text{Joint probability of: [(arrival)(no stroke)]—Line increases by one}$$

$$\mu(1 - \lambda) = Pr[\text{(stroke)(no arrival)}]\text{—Line decreases by one}$$

$$1 - [\mu(1 - \lambda) + \lambda(1 - \mu)] = Pr = [\text{(Line remains the same)}]$$

Figure 5.3 shows both a transition matrix and transition diagram

[8] Consider a night club that is ablaze: if the patrons leave in an orderly fashion, all may escape. If they all try to get out simultaneously, there will be a jamming condition and only a few will get out.

[9] When the vibrator's pulsations per minute are altered, the feed rate changes. This feature is especially important when changing nail sizes.

for the engineer's problem. Suppose that one tube had two nails; locating two on the diagram, it is seen that there are three paths depicting what may occur during the next unit time. One path goes back to one nail, the other loops two and thus remains the same, and the last goes to three, which indicates that the inventory of nails has increased by one. Along these paths are the probabilities for the various events. Thus, going from two to three in one step has a probability of $\lambda(1 - \mu)$. To go from state two to state three in two steps would be

$$P^2_{2,3}[(2 \rightarrow 2 \rightarrow 3) \vee (2 \rightarrow 3 \rightarrow 3)] = \{1 - [\mu(1 - \lambda) + \lambda(1 - \mu)]\}$$
$$[\lambda(1 - \mu)] + [\lambda(1 - \mu)] \cdot \{1 - [\mu(1 - \lambda) + \lambda(1 - \mu)]\},$$

where $$Pr[(2 \rightarrow 2 \rightarrow 3)]$$

is the joint probability of the individual events, going from state two to state two, and state two to state three. The probability for $[(2 \rightarrow 2 \rightarrow 3)]$ is given in the first term of the previous expression. The second term represents the joint probability for the remaining way of going from two to three in two steps. These two terms cannot occur in conjunction, so they are disjointed, mutually exclusive, and their probabilities must be added. Thus the sum of these two terms represents the probability for going from state two to state three in two steps. Finally, notice that this diagram discontinues at four nails because it is impossible to go from four nails back to zero nails in a single step.[10]

The transition matrix of Figure 5.3 contains the same probabilities as the transition diagram. If a tube contains three nails, the probability of its containing two nails after one stroke of the machine is $P^1_{3,2} = \mu(1 - \lambda)$. This matrix is read by first describing the row and then the column. Thus the intersection of row three, column two, is $\mu(1 - \lambda)$; the row indicates the starting state, and the column indicates the finishing state; notation P^1 represents the values of the intersections after a one-step transition.

To find a two-step transition matrix would require that each intersection be replaced by the probabilities for going from one state to another in two distinct steps. For example, it was previously shown that

$$P^2_{2,3} = 2\{1 - [\mu(1 - \lambda) + \lambda(1 - \mu)]\}[\lambda(1 - \mu)]t$$

Continuing this way it would be possible to find all values in the two-step transition, but a swifter way would be to multiply the matrix as follows:

$$P^1 \cdot P^1 = P^2, \ P^1 P^2 = P^3, \ P^1 P^3 = P^4 \dots, \ P^1 \ P^{n-1} = P^n$$

After numerous multiplications all rows would have the same values, which would mean that the transition matrix had reached a fixed state. This is called a steady state in queuing theory. Each row of a probability matrix

[10] John G. Kemeny, Arthur Schleifer, Jr., L. Laurie Snell, Gerald L. Thompson, *Finite Mathematics with Business Applications* (Englewood Cliffs, N.J.: Prentice-Hall, Inc., 1964), pp. 229–311, provides an excellent description of Finite Markov Chains.

Figure 5.3

TRANSITION MATRIX

$$0' = \begin{array}{c} \\ 0 \\ 1 \\ 2 \\ 3 \\ 4 \end{array} \begin{pmatrix} 1-\lambda & \lambda & 0 & 0 & 0 \\ \mu(1-\lambda) & 1-[\mu(1-\lambda)+\lambda(1-\mu)] & \lambda(1-\mu) & 0 & 0 \\ 0 & \mu(1-\lambda) & 1-[\mu(1-\lambda)+\lambda(1-\mu)] & \lambda(1-\mu) & 0 \\ 0 & 0 & \mu(1-\lambda) & 1-[\mu(1-\lambda)+\lambda(1-\mu)] & \lambda(1-\mu) \\ 0 & 0 & 0 & \mu & (1-\mu) \end{pmatrix}$$

TRANSITION DIAGRAM

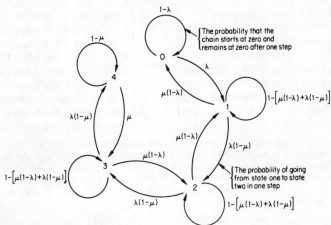

Summary of information contained in Figure 5.3:

Only unit moves occur.

There is no way of going from state three to state one in one step.

It is a Markov chain of discrete parameters with capped line limits.[11]

$0 \wedge 0$	Tube empty and nail does not arrive, $0 \to 0$
$0 \wedge 1$	Tube empty and nail arrives, $0 \to 1$
$2 \wedge 1$	Tube contains two nails, machine strokes, nail does not enter tube, total nails decrease by one, $2 \to 1$
$2 \wedge 2$	No stroke, no arrival, total nails in tube remain the same, $2 \to 2$
$2 \wedge 3$	No stroke, arrival, total nails increase by one, $2 \to 3$
$4 \wedge 3$	Stroke, nail could not arrive because of previously filled tube, $4 \to 3$
$4 \wedge 4$	No stroke, no arrival, tube remains filled, $4 \to 4$

sums to one, so once a matrix has reached this steady state, additional multiplications will be meaningless. Figure 5.4 shows that matrix P^1 approaches a steady state at its 64th power, and thus, continuing with these multiplications, the steady state matrix is developed. These multiplications are at best laborious, but fortunately mathematicians have developed methods

[11] Emanual Parzen, *Stochastic Processes* (San Francisco, Calif.: Holden Day, Inc., 1962).

Figure 5.4

$$
\begin{array}{c}
\quad\quad\quad 0 \quad\quad 1 \quad\quad 2 \quad\quad 3 \quad\quad 4
\end{array}
$$

$$
P^1 = \begin{array}{c} 0 \\ 1 \\ 2 \\ 3 \\ 4 \end{array}
\begin{pmatrix}
0.950 & 0.050 & & & \\
0.114 & 0.842 & 0.044 & & \\
 & 0.114 & 0.842 & 0.044 & \\
 & & 0.114 & 0.842 & 0.044 \\
 & & & 0.120 & 0.880
\end{pmatrix}
\quad
P^{16} = \begin{pmatrix}
0.680 & 0.245 & 0.061 & 0.010 & 0.003 \\
0.562 & 0.286 & 0.112 & 0.032 & 0.007 \\
0.354 & 0.292 & 0.216 & 0.103 & 0.035 \\
0.170 & 0.220 & 0.269 & 0.225 & 0.115 \\
0.070 & 0.136 & 0.246 & 0.313 & 0.235
\end{pmatrix}
$$

$$
P^2 = \begin{pmatrix}
0.908 & 0.090 & 0.002 & & \\
0.204 & 0.720 & 0.074 & 0.002 & \\
0.013 & 0.192 & 0.719 & 0.074 & 0.002 \\
 & 0.013 & 0.192 & 0.719 & 0.076 \\
 & & 0.014 & 0.206 & 0.780
\end{pmatrix}
\quad
P^{32} = \begin{pmatrix}
0.624 & 0.257 & 0.086 & 0.024 & 0.008 \\
0.589 & 0.260 & 0.101 & 0.036 & 0.013 \\
0.501 & 0.261 & 0.137 & 0.069 & 0.031 \\
0.382 & 0.248 & 0.182 & 0.123 & 0.064 \\
0.281 & 0.229 & 0.215 & 0.174 & 0.101
\end{pmatrix} \text{**}
$$

$$
P^4 = \text{*}\begin{pmatrix}
0.843 & 0.146 & 0.010 & & \\
0.334 & 0.551 & 0.107 & 0.007 & \\
0.060 & 0.278 & 0.546 & 0.107 & 0.009 \\
0.005 & 0.056 & 0.278 & 0.547 & 0.114 \\
 & 0.005 & 0.060 & 0.311 & 0.624
\end{pmatrix}
\quad
P^{64} = \begin{pmatrix}
0.595 & 0.257 & 0.098 & 0.036 & 0.013 \\
0.590 & 0.257 & 0.100 & 0.037 & 0.015 \\
0.571 & 0.257 & 0.107 & 0.045 & 0.019 \\
0.541 & 0.256 & 0.119 & 0.057 & 0.026 \\
0.513 & 0.254 & 0.130 & 0.069 & 0.033
\end{pmatrix}
$$

$$
P^8 = \begin{pmatrix}
0.760 & 0.206 & 0.030 & 0.002 & 0.001 \\
0.472 & 0.383 & 0.123 & 0.019 & 0.002 \\
0.177 & 0.320 & 0.359 & 0.122 & 0.022 \\
0.042 & 0.140 & 0.317 & 0.365 & 0.136 \\
0.007 & 0.040 & 0.157 & 0.371 & 0.425
\end{pmatrix}
\quad
P^n = \begin{pmatrix}
0.584 & 0.256 & 0.099 & 0.038 & 0.001 \\
0.584 & 0.256 & 0.099 & 0.038 & 0.001 \\
0.584 & 0.256 & 0.099 & 0.038 & 0.001 \\
0.584 & 0.256 & 0.099 & 0.038 & 0.001 \\
0.584 & 0.256 & 0.099 & 0.038 & 0.001
\end{pmatrix} \text{***}
$$

* These matrices are the squares of their predecessors.

** A matrix is multiplied row vector by column vector. To find the first intersection of P^{64} from P^{32} requires row vector: $(0.624, 0.257, 0.086, 0.024, 0.008)$ multiplies column vector: $(0.624, 0.589, 0.501, 0.382, 0.281) = P^{64}_{0,0} = 0.595$

*** If P^n is squared, it is the same as multiplying P^n by one; it is thus classified as being a steady state.

through which the values of the rows, in the steady-state matrix, are predictable. These row-values will be used in the solution of the engineer's problem.

This problem develops somewhat differently from the previous queuing models in that the line size is capped. Thus with a line size limitation, there is no restriction covering λ/μ. In any queuing model, as μ grows in relation to λ, so grows the probability of having zero units in the system. For a very large μ and a very small λ, say $\lambda/\mu = 3/(4 \times 10^{12})$, then $P_0 \to 1$. In previous discussions it was found that when $\lambda/\mu > 1$, the line increased without limit. This does not hold, however, for the conditions of this example, as the line size is "capped"—limited—to four. Thus as λ/μ grows larger, say $(3 \times 10^{21})/4$, then $P_4 \to 1$ or $P_{n_c} \to 1$, where P_{n_c} = probability when n is capped.

This problem lends itself to solution through Markovian processes owing to its unit-step characteristics. The restrictions governing this solution are: one line, one server, independent exponential arrivals, no special assumptions other than arrivals are probabalistic, and first come–first served discipline.

Two examples are examined. The first is with a $\lambda/\mu < 1$, while the second is a $\lambda/\mu > 1$. The solution-vector principle, expressed as a formula, is introduced instead of using the successive multiplication techniques as previously given in Fig. 5.4. This formula is readily developed from the transition matrix of Fig. 5.3.

Engineers Solutions

Consider the following two possibilities for one tube.

EXAMPLE 1:

$$\frac{\lambda}{\mu} < 1$$

Given: $\lambda = \frac{5}{100} = 0.05$ (Five of one hundred nails are properly aligned when they approach the feeding device.)

$\mu = \frac{12}{100} = 0.12$ (The machine has a capacity of 100 strokes per minute but only twelve are used)

$$
\begin{array}{c}
\begin{array}{ccccc}
0 & 1 & 2 & 3 & 4
\end{array} \\
\begin{array}{c}
0 \\ 1 \\ 2 \\ 3 \\ 4
\end{array}
\left(
\begin{array}{ccccc}
0.950 & 0.050 & & & \\
0.114 & 0.842 & 0.044 & & \\
& 0.114 & 0.842 & 0.044 & \\
& & 0.114 & 0.842 & 0.044 \\
& & & 0.120 & 0.880
\end{array}
\right)
\end{array}
$$

The solution vector to this matrix, when it reaches a steady state, is found through mathematical analysis to be

$$v \approx \frac{(\mu - \lambda)}{\mu(1 - \mu) - \lambda(1 - \lambda)p^4} \, [1 - \mu, p, p^2, p^3, (1 - \lambda)p^4]$$

where

$$p = \frac{P_r \text{ (Line increases by one)}}{P_r \text{ (Line decreases by one)}} = \frac{\lambda(1 - \mu)}{\mu(1 - \lambda)}$$

This vector will yield the following values for P:

$$v = (P_0, P_1, P_2, P_3, P_4)$$

Thus by substitution:

$$p = \frac{\lambda(1 - \mu)}{\mu(1 - \lambda)} = \frac{0.044}{0.114} = 0.38596$$

$$p^2 = 0.14897, \qquad p^3 = 0.05750, \qquad p^4 = 0.00222$$

and the solution vector is:

$$v \approx \frac{0.07000}{0.10560 - 0.04750(0.00222)}$$
$$\times \, [0.880, 0.38596, 0.14896, 0.05749, 0.00222 \, (0.950)]$$

Solution Vector $\approx (0.58392, 0.25610, 0.09885, 0.03815, 0.00140)$

$P_0 \approx 0.584$ (The tube is empty)
$P_1 \approx 0.256$ (The tube contains one nail)
$P_2 \approx 0.099$ (The tube contains two nails)
$P_3 \approx 0.038$ (The tube contains three nails)
$P_4 \approx 0.001$ (The tube is filled)

EXAMPLE 2:

$$\frac{\lambda}{\mu} > 1$$

This is permissible because the line is capped at four.

Given:
$$\lambda = \tfrac{20}{100} = 0.20$$
$$\mu = \tfrac{12}{100} = 0.12$$

$$
\begin{array}{c}
\begin{array}{ccccc}
0 & 1 & 2 & 3 & 4
\end{array} \\
\begin{array}{c}
0 \\ 1 \\ 2 \\ 3 \\ 4
\end{array}
\left(
\begin{array}{ccccc}
0.800 & 0.200 & 0 & 0 & 0 \\
0.096 & 0.728 & 0.176 & & \\
 & 0.096 & 0.728 & 0.176 & \\
 & & 0.096 & 0.728 & 0.176 \\
 & & & 0.120 & 0.880
\end{array}
\right)
\end{array}
$$

$p = 1.83333$, $p^2 = 3.36111$, $p^3 = 6.16204$ $p^4 = 11.29707$

Solution Vector:

$$V \approx \frac{0.12 - 0.20}{0.12(0.88) - 0.20(0.80)(11.29707)}$$
$$\times [0.88000,\ 1.83333,\ 3.36111,\ 6.16204,\ 80(11.29707)]$$
$$\approx [0.04137,\ 0.08618,\ 0.15799,\ 0.28965,\ 0.42482]$$

$P_0 \approx 0.041$ (The tube is empty)
$P_1 \approx 0.086$
$P_2 \approx 0.158$
$P_3 \approx 0.290$
$P_4 \approx 0.425$ (The tube is full)

It follows that for $\lambda/\mu = 0.05/0.12$

$$E_w = \sum_{n=0}^{4} nP_n = 0(0.584) + 1(0.256) + 2(0.099)$$
$$+ 3(0.038) + 4(0.001) = 0.572$$

and for $\lambda/\mu = 0.20/0.12$

$$E_w = \sum_{n=0}^{4} nP_n = 0(0.041) + 1(0.086) + 2(0.158)$$
$$+ 3(0.290) + 4(0.425) = 2.972$$

Thus it appears that a tube that holds four nails will be of sufficient size.

This is contingent on the ability to design a feed slot or orientation device that will correctly present twenty of one hundred nails.

Only two specific cases were studied, one with $P < 1$, and one with $P > 1$. This was undertaken so that some idea could be gained of where E_w begins insuring against a stock-out. These two E_w hold only for the values of $\lambda/\mu = 0.05/0.12$ and $\lambda/\mu = 0.20/0.12$, but they serve as indicators of what may be expected for other values of λ/μ.

5.5 DISCUSSION AND REVIEW QUESTIONS

1. Graph the complementary curve showing the size of the chlorine market as depicted in Fig. 5.2.

2. Suppose that the sales manager of the chlorine sanitizer knew that the market would soon expand to include twenty-five farms. He hypothesized that an intensive sales compaign would result in an improved share of the market for chlorine. If he succeeds, the switch will be one to two instead of the present one to three. What share of the market could he expect? Hint: To cut down on computational work use mathematical tables.

3. Develop your own servicing problem for presentation in class.

4. A nailing machine holds four nails in one slot tube, as given in Sec. 5.4. Determine the solution vector when $\lambda = \frac{4}{5}$ and $\mu = \frac{2}{5}$. Solve also for $\lambda = \frac{1}{5}$ and $\mu = \frac{2}{5}$.

5. Increase the line capacity of Problem 4 so that each slot-tube holds five nails. Solve by squaring the original and successive matrices.

6. Prove that the formula given for the solution vector V in the Markovian example, Sec. 5.4, is correct.

7. Find a formula for the solution vector in Problem 5. Check the results with the solution previously found.

8. In the following computer queuing model check all the results using the formulas given in Chapter 3. Is AVWAT correct? etc.

COMPUTER QUEUING MODEL

Assume that there conditions are given:

	I	II	III
λ	5/hr	7.5/hr	7/hr
μ	5/hr	10/hr	6/hr
H	24 hrs	24 hrs	24 hrs
C_s	$6/hr	$8/hr	$4/hr
C_Q	$8/hr	$12/hr	$9/hr

(NOTATION *to continue on next page*)

NOTATION[12]

$\lambda = $ ARATE	Mean arrival rate	
$\mu = $ SRATE	Mean service rate	
$H = $ HOURS	Hours open for service equals twenty-four in this problem	
$C_Q = $ AWAGE	Cost per unit of time when an arrival is kept waiting prior to being serviced	
$C_s = $ SWAGE	Cost per unit of time to service one arrival	
$E_w = $ AVLEN	Expected number in queue	
$E_t = $ AVWAT	Expected waiting time in line	
$E_\Psi = $ AVTSY	Expected time in system	
$24[E_t(\lambda)] = $ TOWAT	Total waiting time	
$P_0 = $ ZIDLE	(Zero units in system) or idle time rate	
$(P_0)(C_s)(24) = $ ZIDLC	Idle time cost	

(Continued on next page)

Figure 5.5

```
OHIO UNIVERSITY COMPUTER CENTER FORTRAN SYSTEM

NAME          ACCOUNT IDENT SERIAL   DATE OUCC VER 1 MO
WHIPPLE     T U1178   QUEUE 10704   17815                      FYY

/JOB
/FTC     SIZE=128K,NOMAP
BEGIN COMPILATION
          C
          C       SINGLE WAITING LINE  -  POISSON ARRIVAL AND SERVICE RATES
          C
 S.0001        1 FORMAT(5F8.2)
 S.0002        2 FORMAT(/1X'UNACCEPTABLE WAITING LINE')
 S.0003        3 FORMAT(/1X'INFINITE WAITING LINE')
 S.0004        4 FORMAT(/7X'SRATE'5X'ARATE'5X'HOURS'5X'SWAGE'5X'AWAGE')
 S.0005        5 FORMAT(/1X,5F10.2)
 S.0006        6 FORMAT(/4X'AVWAT'3X'AVLEN'3X'AVTSY'3X'TOWAT'3X'ZIDLE'3X'ZIDLC'3X
                1'ARIVL'3X'SCOST'3X'WAITC'3X'TCOST')
 S.0007        7 FORMAT(/1X,9F8.2,F10.2)
 S.0008        8 READ(1,1) SRATE,ARATE,HOURS,SWAGE,AWAGE
 S.0009          IF(SRATE)13,13,9
 S.0010        9 WRITE(3,4)
 S.0011          WRITE(3,5) SRATE,ARATE,HOURS,SWAGE,AWAGE
 S.0012          DIFR=SRATE-ARATE
 S.0013          IF(DIFR)10,11,12
 S.0014       10 WRITE(3,3)
 S.0015          GO TO 8
 S.0016       11 WRITE(3,2)
 S.0017          GO TO 8
 S.0018       12 AVWAT=ARATE/(SRATE*DIFR)
 S.0019          AVLEN=ARATE*AVWAT
 S.0020          AVTSY=1.0/DIFR
 S.0021          ARIVL=ARATE*HOURS
 S.0022          TOWAT=AVWAT*ARIVL
 S.0023          ZIDLE=1.0-ARATE/SRATE
 S.0024          SCOST=SWAGE*HOURS
 S.0025          ZIDLC=ZIDLE*SCOST
 S.0026          WAITC=TOWAT*AWAGE
 S.0027          TCOST=AVTSY*ARIVL*WAITC+SCOST
 S.0028          WRITE(3,6)
 S.0029          WRITE(3,7) AVWAT,AVLEN,AVTSY,TOWAT,ZIDLE,ZIDLC,ARIVL,SCOST,WAITC,
                1TCOST
 S.0030          GO TO 8
 S.0031       13 STOP
 S.0032          END
                 SIZE OF COMMON  00000    PROGRAM  00948
END OF COMPILATION  MAIN
```

[12] IBM Corporation utilizes these techniques in their training sessions and study manuals. This source is recommended for further study involving problems such as question 8, section 5.5.

$$24C_Q[E_t(\lambda)] = \text{WAITC}$$
$$24\{C_s + 24[(E_\Psi)(\lambda^2)(C_Q)(E_t)]\} = \text{TCOST}$$
$$24(\lambda) = \text{ARIVL}$$
$$24(C_s) = \text{SCOST}$$

Waiting cost
Total cost of complete process
Total number of arrivals
Cost for service

Find the following using FORTRAN programming methods. E_w, E_t, E_Ψ, total waiting time, P_0, idle time cost, waiting cost, total number of arrivals, cost for service, and total cost of the complete process for eight hours.

In this problem we have three conditions—they are: $\lambda/\mu = 1$, which is an unacceptable waiting line, $(\lambda/\mu) < 1$, which is acceptable, and $(\lambda/\mu) > 1$, which yields an infinite waiting line. Figure 5.5 gives the compilation, and Fig. 5.6 the printed solution.

Figure 5.6

```
OHIO UNIVERSITY COMPUTER CENTER FORTRAN SYSTEM

/DATA
                                BEGIN LOADING
      STORAGE MAP
 IBCOM   AT LOCATION 001000
*MAIN    AT LOCATION 002450
 MAIN    AT LOCATION 002458


     SRATE      ARATE     HOURS      SWAGE      AWAGE

     5.00       5.00      24.00      6.00       8.00

UNACCEPTABLE WAITING LINE

     SRATE      ARATE     HOURS      SWAGE      AWAGE

     10.00      7.50      24.00      8.00       12.00

   AVWAT   AVLEN   AVTSY   TOWAT   ZIDLE   ZIDLC   ARIVL   SCOST   WAITC   TCOST

   0.30    2.25    0.40    54.00   0.25    48.00   180.00  192.00  648.00  46847.97

     SRATE      ARATE     HOURS      SWAGE      AWAGE

     6.00       7.00      24.00      4.00       9.00

INFINITE WAITING LINE

TOTAL JOB TIME FOR 10704 IS 0043.10 SECONDS
```

9. Write a flow chart for Problem 8

10. Develop a flow chart for a constant service time queuing model to find the same value as given in Problem 8

11. Develop a flow chart for a single line, single server finite queuing model. Show how to find E_w, E_t, E_Ψ, and E_n.

6.   Simulation

6.1 NATURE AND MEANING OF SIMULATION

Behaviorists use a game to prove that man, when subjected to repeated trials, will eventually develop patterns and regularities in his decision-processes. The game is presented in the following manner: "Choose a number from one to ten and I will give you one dollar for every time I miss, if you give me seven dollars for every time I guess correctly. You may change your number with every trial". This certainly appears to be a game favoring those who accept the wager but, given a number of trials, a shrewd analyst will have the pattern figured and the game will then be in his favor. The behaviorist will lose this game, however, if the bettor selects his numbers at random.

Random numbers are found in many ways. Some of the more popular methods to generate random numbers are logarithmic, midsquare, and probabilistic methods. There are also random-numbers tables which are included in many mathematical textbooks; this eliminates the necessity for generating your own tables in most elementary analysis. As in the previous game, random numbers are similarly important to queuing theory. They are used to help simulate models not easily solved through conventional mathematical procedures, and thus are in wide use today, especially in application involving the computer.

Techniques of simulation have been known for many years. Some of these were readily usable while others were only of theoretical interest until the development of high-speed electronic computers. Simulation in early history could broadly be interpreted as any analog (an abstraction of reality). It is possible that one of man's first simulations was a series of pictures on the wall of a cave depicting an idea or event, another could have been his language—words are certainly abstractions, and, when spoken, only simulate those things observed or experienced. Think of the first working model of a Roman catapult; consider machines that open and shut refrigerator-doors to determine life expectancy of components; and for a last example consider astronauts' flight simulators. All of these are simulators, but what of simulation and mathematics?

Simulation techniques were not unknown to early mathematicians— they only lacked the vehicle to carry them out. They knew that the internal heat of an irregularly shaped object, with numerous and different surface temperatures, could be found by simulation techniques using random walk- ing principles, but this technique required so many successive trials that it was not considered practical. Their solution utilized a sophisticated method called Laplace transformations. Today, with the high-speed computer, persons with a somewhat limited knowledge may work this problem, using simulation techniques; in fact many programmers use computers to inves- tigate problems that in the past were reserved exclusively for those possess- ing an advanced knowledge of mathematics.[1]

Queuing theory is a good example of this transition because simulation can be used extensively for investigating complex queuing problems that were previously in the domain of those few persons capable of dealing in the abstract. This is not to imply that queuing models of today do not require abstract thinking; it serves only to illustrate the fact that simulation has simplified the analysis of some models that were originally quite complex. As in all studies, there are the elementary and difficult subjects; this is par- ticularly true of simulation. While it has made some of the previously com- plex subjects easy to solve, simulation as a separate topic has grown into an advanced mathematical study. This, of course, is characteristic of scientific inquiry. The previously complex subjects become easier to comprehend, which in turn allows for more time in which to simplify what is new; thus the cycle is continuous.

Not all simulation techniques require a random number table, but one method utilizes this extensively: it is known as Monte Carlo simulation.[2] Historically, this technique owes its acceptance to those many persons who pioneered in its use. Rather than study individuals, it may be interesting to note a few basic reasons why simulation techniques, including Monte Carlo, were developed. This may be done by associating simulation tech- niques with examples arising from the history of science.

Some of the first uses of simulation began with the study of evolution, in which man attempted to associate his past with how he evolved. Another use arose when mathematicians used a repeating-trials process to solve quartic equations. In a broad sense, these investigations may be called simu- lations, but not with today's restrictive connotation. Modern simulation,

---

[1] A computer does not solve a problem; it assists men in the solution of problems involving a large amount of computation. Such men, of high competence and skill, are required to provide the computer with the method of solution; the computer simply follows the method, repeating it as often as needed.

[2] The name Monte Carlo is immediately associated with gaming tables, where many concepts of probabilities are empirically discovered. Here is seen at first hand the truth of the old adage, "Some learn from experience while others do not."

particularly Monte Carlo, had its beginning in statistical model sampling. With this technique statistical samples are used to build models that approximate the supplying universe. In this process a random-numbers table is used to guarantee that each sample represents an unbiased subset coming from the original population, and also that each event is independent of its predecessor. Given a correctly-chosen sample size and number of trials, statisticians have developed probabilistic formulas for predicting the parameters of the supplying universe; thus it is interesting to note that simulation developed from a numerous-trials process with qualitative limitations, to one of numerous trials with quantitative limitations.

Notice that, by implication, simulation techniques such as Monte Carlo are usually reserved for exceptionally difficult tasks where the scientist has difficulty associating his observed data with a known mathematical distribution or formulation; for tasks where the distributions are known but no algebraic method is available to aid in the solution of the problem; and for other situations not readily solved by conventional mathematics. Simulation techniques, however, are only as good as the original model that has been created abstractly by the scientist. If this original abstraction is filled with personal bias, the simulated model may be restricted—bound to find only those prejudicial results. The true scientist usually does not fall into this trap, but history can provide us with thousands of other examples, such as the "scientific" justification of the superiority of race or class, mathematical developments proving the inevitability of afterlife, etc.[3] Man generally scoffs at those old and exploded theories, but how many are believed today that will be proved wrong tomorrow?

The precautionary message is given here to drive home the idea that if an incorrect hypothesis is followed by correct quantitative analysis, there still remains a high probability that the conclusion is wrong. Some persons in the scientific-business world become married to their ideas, which in turn are responsible for many problems that are not necessarily filtered out by the magic of number-manipulation.

6.2 MONTE CARLO TECHNIQUES

Monte Carlo techniques, when applied to queuing problems, have many distinct advantages over an algebraic approach, such as: (a) Disci-

---

[3] The French General Staff used science to convict Captain Alfred Dreyfus of treason—even though the majority of other scientists called upon to participate in this investigation considered him innocent. The army's investigators would only accept as "expert testimony" those scientific proofs that agreed with their predetermined beliefs; thus, science was used to prove an incorrect hypothesis. The *Dreyfus Method of Analysis* is causing many business problems today.

plines other than first come–first served may be readily investigated; (b) Service and arrival distributions are not restricted to Poisson arrivals and exponential or Erlang service times; (c) Station-to-station queuing problems are generally easier to simulate rather than solve algebraically; and (d) simulation is easier to explain to the nonquantitative executive since he may visually trace the element through the system rather than handle it abstractly. Continuing with this Monte Carlo comparison, simulation is found to have these advantages over sampling theory: it is faster; the analyst has control of the process; and discipline may be changed. This flexibility allows him to experiment with various ideas for improving the system.

In general, Monte Carlo is favored by analysts because it allows them to develop synthetic data and thus avoid the expense and time of gathering historical information. Tables 4.3 and 4.4 of Sec. 4.5 show the actual and theoretical data for the Obstetrical Department. To collect these data required the services of one business manager and two stenographers. Most averages were known prior to their gathering because the hospital kept records of patient stay and house census. The reason for collecting the data was to verify the distribution. If another hospital were analyzed, the Poisson distribution could be assumed. Thus with the arithmetical means readily available, most expense and time could be eliminated. In fact, the theoretical Poisson distribution would be more reliable than the historically gathered data owing to inadequacies of the empirical data with respect to sample size. Remember that the historical data must be tested against a known mathematical distribution before the latter replaces the former. This was done in Table 4.3. Historical data are often unavailable, sometimes because they represent proprietary information of the corporation; often they are inconvenient to use because they come from many sections and there has not been a uniform collecting method. An analyst may chose to make some assumptions concerning the characteristics of the actual statistical distribution, and then proceed with the simulation. Historical data may be used in preference to synthetic data if the actual data do not follow a known distribution; but the sample size of the actual distribution must be large enough to assure reliability. There is danger in the procedure since the fluctuations of the variables from historical distributions may become repetitious, thus destroying much of the randomness.

6.3 USE OF RANDOM NUMBERS IN MONTE CARLO SIMULATION

Random numbers may be generated through various methods, but in order to simplify elementary computational procedures, mathematicians have developed numerous random-number tables; one of these is given in Table 6.23 at the end of this chapter.

6.31 Example 1

The following example shows how to utilize random numbers when employing Monte Carlo techniques:

Given historical data showing the life expectancy of truck batteries, is it possible to determine how many batteries will be required over the next twelve years?

Table 6.1

Months of use before replacement	Frequency expressed as a percent	Random numbers
12	4%	00–03*
16	7	04–10
20	13	11–23
24	17	24–40
28	27	41–67
32	11	68–78
36	7	79–85
40	6	86–91
44	5	92–96
48	3	97–99

* Since there are four machines in the group 00–03, they represent four percent of the 100 numbers used.

This problem is readily approached through Monte Carlo simulation techniques that incorporate a random-numbers table. As seen in Table 6.1, four percent of the batteries only last twelve months, seven percent last thirty six months, etc. The random-numbers table included in this book theoretically embodies numbers from 00000–99999. In this example there is need for only the first two digits, so selection of a set of ten numbers from column 1 yields the data of Table 6.2.

Table 6.2

Battery	Random Number	Number Utilized	Months of Use
A	96268	96	44
B	03550	03	12
C	22188	22	20
D	63759	63	28
E	55006	55	28
F	81972	81	36
G	06344	06	16
H	92363	92	44
I	96083	96	44
J	92993	92	44

Table 6.3

Battery	Month of Use before Replacement						
	Trial 1	2	3	4	5	6	7
A	44	20	24	16	28	36	
B	12	16	24	32	32	24	20
C	20	44	16	28	48		
D	28	36	28	28	28		
E	28	20	28	24	28		
F	36	28	28	28	44		
G	16	24	24	32	28	32	
H	44	20	44	20	28		
I	44	40	24	44			
J	44	36	28	20	24		

Continuing with the same methods, the simulated data shown in Table 6.3 can be developed. Note that Battery B would be replaced seven times while battery I would be replaced only four times during the 144-month period. The conclusion is that a total of fifty-three batteries will be needed over the next twelve years. Remember that this is only one trial, which may be a unique case, so that a number of such trials would be required. Figure 6.1 depicts the cumulative results of a number of such trials. In the selection of the random numbers for this model, each set of ten numbers was selected from a different starting position. This helps to maintain randomness; but would not this starting-point selection-process soon develop patterns and regularities as with the game of chance played with the behaviorist? This precautionary note is sounded only to keep a prospective user apprised of what may happen.

Figure 6.1

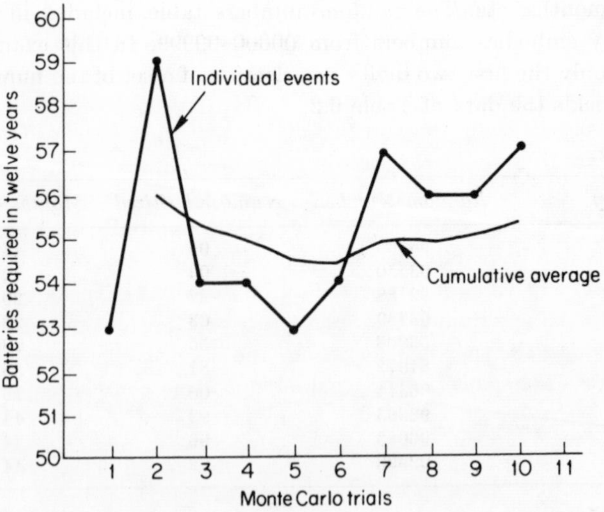

The cumulative line of Fig. 6.1 clearly indicates that this process has not been operating long enough to reach a position of little variation; this means that additional trials should be conducted. After it stabilizes, however, it will only give what may be expected. Considering the individual trials, we observe that management had better be prepared for these because wide variations will occur and may prove disastrous to those who are prepared for an average.

Many analysts continue these trials until the cumulative line variation is minimal, i.e., rate of change approaches zero. Fundamental statistical techniques from sampling theory may also be used for testing when the system has approximately produced the real-life model.[4] Even with these techniques the analyst is often forced to make subjective decisions owing to fundamental problems associated with the gathering of original data. An experiment with this process will prove to be a laborious lesson, but the same procedure when carried out by a computer relieves man of an exceptionally time-consuming task.

6.4 MONTE CARLO APPLIED TO QUEUING PROBLEMS

The Monte Carlo approach requires an evaluation of numerous individual examples randomly chosen. To illustrate this concept it will prove advantageous to investigate the following examples.

6.41 Example I (one line, one server model)

Situation

During winter months, workers in one department complain constantly about the cold air that blows on them whenever their overhead door is used by fork-truck drivers. The situation magnifies, as door-usage increases, to the extent that many workers leave their machines whenever the door is opened. Productivity suffers and this unquestionably disturbs management. The door is finally placed on a one minute time-delay relay system, with positive safety features that operate automatically as trucks use the doors. This reduces time through the door as drivers no longer must quit their vehicles to operate the door switches, and it also eliminates the spiteful lingering for a long while as the machine operators complain.

[4] Giuseppe M. Ferrero di Roccaferrera, *Operations Research Models for Business and Industry* (Southwestern Publishing Company, Cincinnati, Ohio, 1964,) pp. 873–879 for an explanation of queues with regard to sampling theory.

This solution only relieves the individual situation, for again with the increased usage the department is cold. Heating and ventilating engineers recommend the use of an air lock, which uses two doors automatically timed so that one truck requires two minutes through the system. This will stop the cold blast of air and save fuel, but will delay trucks since only one can use this door-system at one time. A suggestion from one of the workers in the department recommends that an air door, similar to those doors made of air in department stores, be installed so that this will give free entrance and exits without delay or discomfort to the workers.

Investigations reveal that use of this door is extremely heavy and that the trucks cannot be sent along another route since this would result in a considerable delay.

Analysis

An analysis of truck arrival times is found to have the following probability distribution shown in Table 6.4.

Table 6.4

Minutes Between Arrivals	Probability	Monte Carlo Numbers
0	0.028	001–028
1	0.201	029–229
2	0.267	230–496
3	0.226	497–722
4	0.160	723–882
5	0.075	883–957
6	0.026	958–983
7	0.010	984–993
8	0.005	994–998
9	0.001	999
10	0.001	000

To simulate this process it is essential that: (a) Imput and output data be shown in terms of a probability distribution, given that enough observations have been made to assure reliability; (b) The probability distribution be expressed as random numbers; (c) Columns be set up to depict how one element passes through the system in a chosen unit time; and (d) Enough individual experiments are conducted to assure reliability.

In Table 6.5 the simulation begins with one truck in the air lock. This first line reads, "The number 186 taken from the random-number table shows one minute elapsed between this arrival and its immediate predecessor. This truck cannot be immediately processed because there is another truck in the air lock requiring an additional minute of servicing time. The incoming truck must therefore wait one minute until its servicing commences. After servicing, the truck departs at time-block four having spent three minutes in the system; the air lock was completely utilized during this first sample."

Additional examples show: (a) At time-block fifteen, two trucks arrive simultaneously; (b) Time-block forty-two indicates that the door is not utilized for three minutes because it was empty at time-block thirty-nine minutes without any demand for service until the forty-second minute; and (c) A truck requires service during the twenty-seventh minute but cannot be accepted into the system until three minutes later because the door is not cleared until that time and also because other trucks are before it, given a first come–first served discipline regardless of which side of the door is approached.

From the thirty-one randomly selected numbers shown in Table 6.5,

Table 6.5

SIMULATION OF TRUCKS THROUGH PROPOSED AIR-LOCK

Random Number	Minutes Between Arrivals	Time Truck Arrives at Door	Minutes Truck Waits	Truck Through Door	Minutes Door Not Utilized
186	1	1	1	4	0
914	5	6	0	8	2
120	1	7	1	10	0
142	1	8	2	12	0
776	4	12	0	14	0
564	3	15	0	17	1
013	0	15	2	19	0
978	6	21	0	23	2
694	3	24	0	26	1
074	1	25	1	28	0
029	1	26	2	30	0
072	1	27	3	32	0
962	6	33	0	35	1
748	4	37	0	39	2
920	5	42	0	44	3
097	1	43	1	46	0
539	3	46	0	48	0
337	2	48	0	50	0
299	2	50	0	52	0
020	0	50	2	54	0
723	4	54	0	56	0
685	3	57	0	59	1
421	2	59	0	61	0
544	3	62	0	64	1
530	3	65	0	67	1
158	1	66	1	69	0
997	8	74	0	76	5
358	2	76	0	78	0
219	1	77	1	80	0
692	3	80	0	82	0
809	4	84	0	86	2
Totals	84		17		22

$\frac{84}{31} = 2.70968$ min (average arrival time), $\frac{17}{31} = 0.54838$ min (average waiting time) per truck)

$\frac{22}{31} = 0.70967$ min (average lost servicing opportunity)

eighty-four minutes transpired, seventeen minutes of waiting time were required for thirty-one trucks, and the door was not used for twenty-two minutes. These data, however, are far from being representative as they have not been simulated through enough trials. To give some idea how this varies, two individual trials of sixty-seven experiments were conducted with the following results:

Number of Experiments	Minutes Between Arrivals	Truck Waiting Time	Minutes Door Not Utilized	Average Arrival Time (min)	Average Waiting Time (min)	Average Lost Servicing Opportunity (min)
67	197	25	61	2.94	0.373	0.910
67	176	34	42	2.63	0.507	0.627
134	373	59	103	2.78	0.440	0.769

These two trials vary considerably, which shows that there is a great probability of obtaining biased results if the sample size is too small; if, however, this total sample size of 134 trials were adequate, then a cost analysis could be undertaken.

Cost Data

Engineers have calculated: the average cost to reheat air for seven months of use = \$0.250/opening; cost of air lock system = \$12,500 (\$8000 door plus installation, and \$4500 for space costs); cost of air door = \$37,500; days of use per year = 152; truck cost per hour = \$9.73 (includes lost opportunity).

Cost Analysis Air Lock (Three Shifts—Twenty-Four Hour Day)

a. $\dfrac{24 \text{ hrs}}{\text{day}} \times \dfrac{60 \text{ min}}{1 \text{ hr}} \times \dfrac{1 \text{ arrival}}{2.78 \text{ min}} = \dfrac{517.32 \text{ arrivals}}{\text{day}}$

b. $\dfrac{517.32 \text{ arrivals}}{\text{day}} \times \dfrac{0.44 \text{ min waiting}}{\text{arrival}} \times \dfrac{1 \text{ hr}}{60 \text{ min}} = \dfrac{3.79 \text{ hrs of waiting}}{\text{day}}$

c. Process time = $2 \text{ min} \times \dfrac{\text{hr}}{60 \text{ min}} \times \dfrac{517.32 \text{ arrivals}}{\text{day}} = \dfrac{17.24 \text{ hrs}}{\text{day}}$

d. Cost of waiting = $\dfrac{\$9.73}{\text{hr}} \times \dfrac{3.79 \text{ hrs of waiting}}{\text{day}} = \dfrac{\$36.88}{\text{day}}$

e. Cost of service = $\dfrac{\$9.73}{\text{hr}} \times \dfrac{17.24 \text{ hrs}}{\text{day}} = \dfrac{\$167.75}{\text{day}}$

f. Total cost = $\dfrac{36.88 + 167.75}{\text{day}} = \dfrac{\$204.63}{\text{day}}$

g. Average yearly cost (152 days) = $\dfrac{\$31,103.76}{\text{yr}}$

Table 6.6 shows a comparison of these two proposals.

Table 6.6

		Air Lock	Air Door
Cost of Facility		$12,500	$37,500*
Waiting Time	(517.32)(0.44/60)	3.79 hrs/day	0**
Processing Time	(517.32)(2/60)	17.24 hrs/day	0
Waiting Cost	(9.73)(3.79)	$36.88	0
Servicing Cost	(9.73)(17.24)	$167.75	0
Total Daily Cost	(36.88 + 167.75)	$204.63	0
Days System Used		152/yr	152/yr
Total Service Cost	(204.63)(152)	$31,103.76/yr	0

* The cost of the air door could be justified solely from the total service cost of the air lock vs. air door if the slightly higher costs of maintaining an air door were disregarded.

** This table shows that there is zero cost for truck processing through an air door system. Theoretically there is that rare possibility of demand being so heavy, in one time period, that some waiting will occur. This is very small, and costs are minimal. Air doors when improperly designed for traffic can also present some waiting time, but not in this situation.

Conclusion

In the actual situation management did not adopt either the air lock or air door system even through the present system resulted in an exceptionally high fuel cost.[5] This is not unusual, since requests for moneys usually exceed what is available. Management must therefore give up a desirable program, much like an individual who must pass up an exceptional value in mink coats when his resources meet only the basic needs for sustenance.

6.42 Example II (station-to-station model)

Situation

To relieve the stresses following a forming operation, glass is usually annealed in a furnace, called a lehr. At the end of the lehr, additional operations such as inspection, screwing on of the cap, placement in the carton, and packaging are completed. It is extremely expensive to stop the lehr because this means that a costly series of machine will be delayed; these machines automatically feed their completed products onto the lehr conveyor belt; the belt has a take-away speed greater than the machine feed, which eliminates damage or jamming between completed parts. If the lehr is

---

[5] $0.250 (152)(517.32) = $19,658.16. Remember that this $0.250 is an average based upon the weather bureau's mean average temperature for these months of door usage. On days when the air is reheated from $-15°F$ to $72°F$, the cost is much higher. Similarly, numbers derived from simulation are based on generated data which also could represent a biased example.

stopped, either the machines are stopped or its products stored, which results in a considerable cost to the company.

Data

The system has the configuration shown in Fig. 6.2.

1. Culture-tube machine operates at 93.2% efficiency and is set at sixty-five cycles per minute. Thus, $(93.2\%)(65) = 60.58$, which is the average culture tubes manufactured by each machine.
2. The lehr take-away speed is synchronous to the operation.
3. Three culture-tube machines feed three separate lines on the lehr.

Figure 6.2

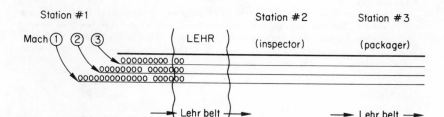

Station #2   Inspect, screw on cap, place in carton

Station #3   Pack cartons into case

4. Station One has the following output characteristics for one machine:

Pieces/minute	Frequency	Random Number Range*
54	2	0001–0002
55	27	0003–0029
56	98	0030–0128
57	341	0129–0469
58	841	0470–1310
59	1527	1311–2839
60	2198	2840–5037
61	2206	5038–7243
62	1601	7244–8845
63	827	8846–9672
64	227	9673–9901
65	99	9902–0000
	9994	

* The random numbers were found by converting the frequencies into probabilities and then assigning the correct random-number range.
$\frac{341}{9994} = 0.3412 \approx 0.341$, which accounts for the random-number range of 0.0129 − 0.0469.

5. Station Two has the following distribution of times:

Minutes/150 Pieces	Pieces/Minute	Observed Frequency	Random Number Range
$\frac{1}{4}$	600	27	0001–0591
$\frac{2}{4}$	300	141	0592–3676
$\frac{3}{4}$	200	156	3677–7089
$\frac{4}{4}$	150	98	7090–9233
$\frac{5}{4}$	120	19	9234–9649
$\frac{6}{4}$	100	11	9650–9890
$\frac{7}{4}$	36	4	9891–9978
$\frac{8}{4}$	75	1	9979–0000
		457	

Notice that the input data were given in minutes per 150 pieces. In order to conduct this simulation properly, all stations must be measured in equivalent units. This accounts for the additional pieces/minute column.

6. Station Three has the following distribution of times required for packing one gross of culture tubes to the case:

Minutes	Pieces/Minute	Observed Frequency	Random Number Range
$\frac{1}{8}$	1152	4	0001–0084**
$\frac{2}{8}$	576	19	0085–0481
$\frac{3}{8}$	384*	51	0482–1545
$\frac{4}{8}$	288	99	1546–3611
$\frac{5}{8}$	230	119	3612–6095
$\frac{6}{8}$	192	74	6096–7639
$\frac{7}{8}$	165	32	7640–8307
$\frac{8}{8}$	144	22	8308–8766
$\frac{9}{8}$	128	16	8767–9100
$\frac{10}{8}$	115	11	9101–9330
$\frac{11}{8}$	105	8	9331–9497
$\frac{12}{8}$	96	7	9498–9643
$\frac{13}{8}$	89	4	9644–9727
$\frac{14}{8}$	82	3	9728–9790
$\frac{15}{8}$	77	1	9791–9811
$\frac{16}{8}$	72	4	9812–9895
$\frac{17}{8}$	68	1	9896–9916
$\frac{18}{8}$	64	2	9917–9958
$\frac{19}{8}$	61	1	9959–9979
$\frac{20}{8}$	58	1	9980–0000
		479	

* $(\frac{8}{3})(144) = 384$ pieces per minute
** $\frac{4}{479} = 0.0084$, which accounts for the random-number range of 0001–0084

Five separate random numbers were chosen for each line of Table 6.7. The random numbers for line 1 were: 4719, 2982, 7642, 6242, 0591, which represent $(60 + 60 + 62) = 182$ for station 1, 200 for station 2, and 384 for station 3. Line 15 of this table reads: Machines A, B, C, were found to produce sixty-two, sixty-one, and sixty culture tubes respectively, for a total of one hundred eighty-three pieces. Servicing capacity at station 2 was one hundred twenty pieces; therefore a queue of sixty-three pieces developed. This, when added to the previous queue, yields an inventory of eighty-nine pieces at station 2. Output of station 2 governs the input of station 3; therefore station 3, with an output of 165 pieces, receives only 120 pieces from station 2. This results in a reduction of forty-five pieces in the queue of culture tubes previously formed $(132 - 45 = 87)$.

The machines and stations of this problem are spaced many minutes apart. To envision how this simulation works, consider that outputs from one station are not tabulated until they arrive at the next. A queue may build up a number of ways on a conveyor. Sometimes the parts are stopped but the conveyor continues to move beneath them. At other times a relief operator is called to inventory the parts in partially-filled cartons or cases. Other inventory schemes include allowing the personnel to move up or down the line and the creation of areas for the banking of parts.

Table 6.7

SIMULATION OF CULTURE TUBES THROUGH THREE STATIONS ON LEHR BELT

	STATION 1			STATION 2			STATION 3		
Elapsed Time	Machine Output			Number Arriving	Servicing Capacity	Queue Size	Number Arriving	Servicing Capacity	Queue Size
	A	B	C						
1	60	60	62	182	200	0	182	384	0
2	60	60	61	181	150	31	150	115	35
3	60	63	65	188	200	19	200	192	43
4	62	62	59	183	300	0	202	128	117
5	59	62	59	180	300	0	180	192	105
6	64	55	58	177	300	0	177	288	0
7	58	58	60	176	300	0	176	96	80
8	60	62	63	185	200	0	185	192	73
9	60	60	63	183	200	0	183	72	184
10	63	59	58	180	200	0	180	89	275
11	64	65	61	190	300	0	190	165	300
12	58	60	63	181	300	0	181	288	193
13	62	60	60	182	300	0	182	165	210
14	57	61	58	176	150	26	150	192	132
15	62	61	60	183	120	89	120	165	87
16	62	58	58	178	150	117	150	128	109
17	57	59	61	177	200	94	200	576	0
18	61	65	62	188	200	82	200	384	0
19	58	60	57	175	150	107	150	165	0
20	59	60	56	175	150	132	150	165	0
21	58	59	62	179	200	111	200	64	136
22	63	62	61	183	300	0	294	288	142
23	63	62	61	186	200	0	186	230	98
24	60	61	62	183	200	0	183	230	51
25	60	58	59	177	300	0	177	230	0
Total	1508	1511	1509	4528	5570	808	4528	5183	2370
Averages	60.32	60.44	60.36	181.12	222.8	32.32	181.12	207.32	94.80

A culture tube is six inches long with a one-inch diameter. It proceeds down the belt by diameter, so five culture tubes require five inches. The maximum of inches required at station 2 was 132, and at station 3, 300. The maximums may easily exceed these figures, but 300 inches is extremely expensive in terms of space and unoccupied lehr belt. What must be measured in these situations is the cost of making an operation more synchronous, relief-operator cost versus additional space, additional costs for damaged pieces, etc. If the input machines may produce a variety of shapes and pieces, then the operations becomes more difficult to maximize. These problems are not insurmountable, however, because competent analysts may readily simulate more complex problems with the aid of a computer.

Analysis

Twenty-five simulations of Table 6.7 of this station-to-station queue, while not a significantly large sample, will give some insight into the queue lengths formed at each station.

Conclusion

From the abbreviated simulation of Table 6.44, it is possible to gather the machine averages, each station's average servicing capacity, and the average queue-sizes. From this an analyst could design a better system when all products and sizes serviced by the lehr were included in the study. With a computer it would be practical to try a number of different inputs and disciplines at each station, thus theoretically finding the most economical set of parts, feeds, and speeds at which they should operate. The fact that station 2 builds up and depletes is indicative of acceptable station 1 and 2 relationships. Stations 2 and 3, however, seem to have an improper relationship due to the queue sizes formed, even though they occasionally deplete. As stated before, the analyst for this job would make numerous trials until he arrived at a satisfactory combination.[6] This could result in additional crew, new line inventorying, new procedures, or other changes.

6.43 EXAMPLE III (One Line, Multiple Server)[7]

Data

Machinists obtain tools from clerks, at a tool crib, when these require replacements. Suppose for the purpose of this example that: (a) Each clerk

---

[6] A satisfactory, instead of optimal, combination. Attempting to find an optimal solution through simulation is a costly process because of time and efficiency.

[7] Adapted from John G. Kemeny, Arthur Schleifer, Jr., J. Laurie Snell, and Gerald Thompson, *Finite Mathematics with Business Applications* [Prentice-Hall, Inc, Englewood Cliffs, N. J., pp. 207–210 (converted to FORTRAN Language with flow chart and printouts for use in this book)].

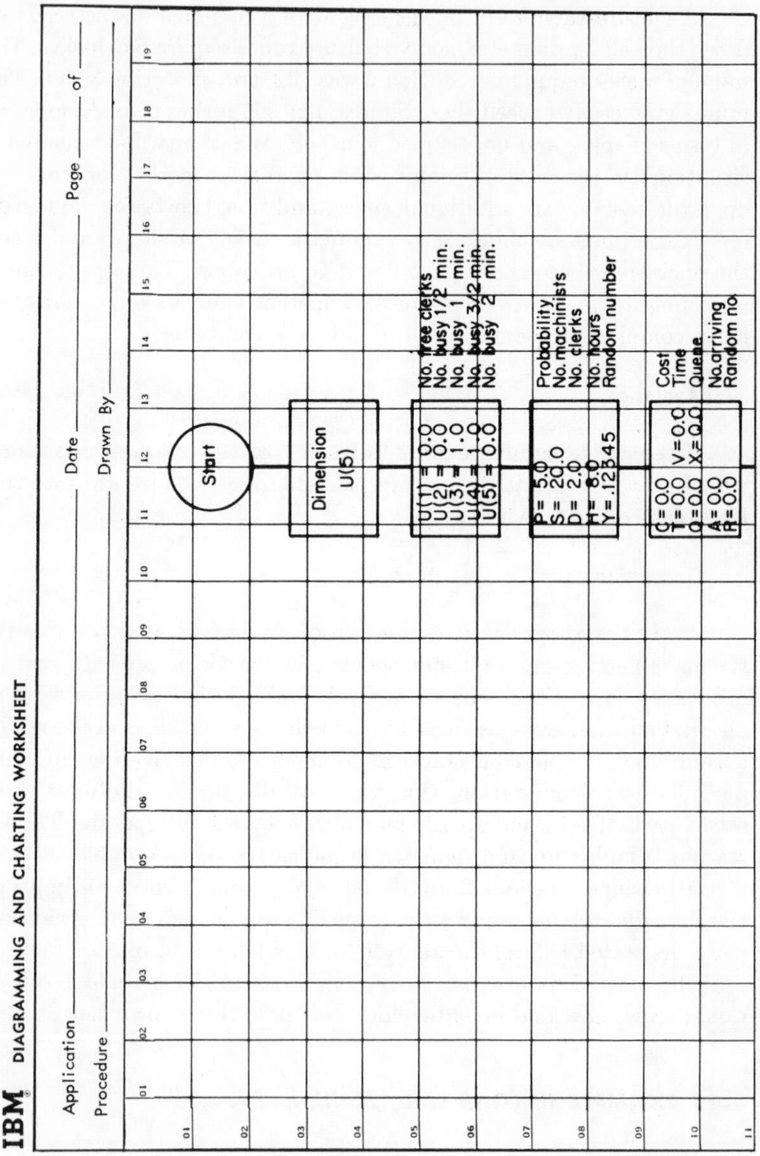

Figure 6.3

IBM DIAGRAMMING AND CHARTING WORKSHEET

Application _____ Date _____ Page ___ of ___
Procedure _____ Drawn By _____

Start

Dimension
U(5)

U(1) = 0.0   No. free clerks
U(2) = 0.0   No. busy 1/2 min.
U(3) = 1.0   No. busy 1 min.
U(4) = 1.0   No. busy 3/2 min.
U(5) = 0.0   No. busy 2 min.

P = 5.0   Probability
S = 20.0   No. machinists
D = 2.0   No. clerks
H = 8.0   No. hours
Y = .12345   Random number

C = 0.0   V = 0.0   Cost
T = 0.0   Time
Q = 0.0   X = 0.0   Queue
A = 0.0   No. arriving
R = 0.0   Random no.

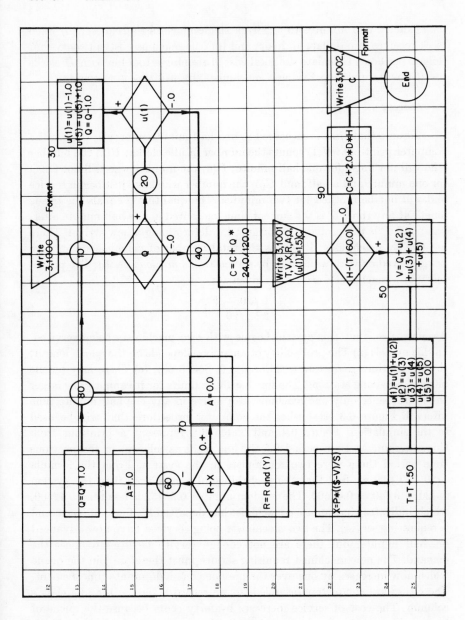

uses exactly two minutes to service a single machinist's request; (b) Each
clerk receives two dollars an hour; and (c) Idle machine cost is twenty-four
dollars per hour. Calculate the total cost of running a tool bin with D clerks
for H hours, in a shop having S machinists, by utilizing a computer.

Analysis

Assume that time is measured in one-half minute intervals; then in the
computer print-out: $U(1)$ counts the number of idle clerks; $U(2)$ the number
who will not finish for one-half minute; $U(3)$ the number who will not finish
for one minute and a half; and $U(5)$ the number who have just begun service
and will not be finished for two minutes. The quantity Q equals the queue
length at any time; T is the current time, measured in one-half minute intervals; and P is the probability formula for determining a new arrival. There
are twenty machinists. V counts the total number of machinists who were
being served or were waiting to be served *in the previous period*. The probability of a machinist's arriving is given as:

$$\frac{1}{2}\left(\frac{20-V}{20}\right)$$

Assume, also, that this system begins with two machinists being serviced.
In this model: (a) The probability of an arrival depends on the queue length;
(b) Service time is constant (see Chapter 3, Sec. 3.65); (c) There may be one
or more servicing stations. The line has finite limits for it cannot grow larger
than four, since only one machinist can arrive in any one-half minute time
interval. Figure 6.3 establishes the computer procedure that will be used
in the simulation. Figure 6.4 and Table 6.8 represent a print-out from
this program. At time period 9.5 the line reads as follows: in the previous
time period there were two machinists in the system. From the formula
$\frac{1}{2}(20-V)/20$ we find that the probability of a new arrival in the system
is $(20-3)/40 = 0.42500$. The random number 0.30459 is less than 0.42500,
which indicates that another machinist has departed his finite universe and
is requesting service. The two machinists being serviced have now advanced
one-half minute, but there are not enough service facilities to meet the
demand. The new machinist requiring service must therefore join the queue
which now increases by one over the previous one-half minute time element.
The clerks are completely occupied, so we record a zero in the idle clerk's
columm. The cost of service increases by forty cents because the queue of
two machinists represents a machine idle-time cost of: $2(\$24/120) = \$0.40$.
This model may be readily hand-simulated. It is included here, however,
to illustrate two basic queuing applications—they are: how to program a
simulation problem, and how a one-line multiple server problem develops.

```
OHIO UNIVERSITY COMPUTER CENTER FORTRAN SYSTEM

NAME           ACCOUNT IDENT SERIAL  DATE OUCC VER 1 MO
WHIPPLE    T  U1178  WAIT   10703   17815                    FYY

/JOB
/FTC      SIZE=128K,NOMAP
BEGIN COMPILATION
              C
              C        WAITING LINE PROBLEM
              C
              C        U(1)=NUMBER FREE CLERKS
              C        U(2)=NUMBER BUSY 1/2 MINUTE
              C        U(3)=NUMBER BUSY 1 MINUTE
              C        U(4)=NUMBER BUSY 3/2 MINUTES
              C        U(5)=NUMBER BUSY 2 MINUTES
              C        P=PROBABILITY
              C        S=NUMBER MACHINISTS
              C        D=NUMBER CLERKS
              C        H=NUMBER HOURS
              C        C=COST
              C        T=TIME
              C        Q=QUEUE
              C        A=NUMBER ARRIVING
              C
              C        STORAGE ALLOCATIONS
              C
  S.0001               DIMENSION U(5)
              C
              C        INITIALIZE CONSTANTS
              C
  S.0002               U(1)=0.
  S.0003               U(2)=0.
  S.0004               U(3)=1.
  S.0005               U(4)=1.
  S.0006               U(5)=0.
  S.0007               P=.50
  S.0008               S=20.0
  S.0009               D=2.0
  S.0010               H=8.0
  S.0011               Y=.12345
  S.0012               C=0.0
  S.0013               T=0.0
  S.0014               Q=0.0
  S.0015               A=0.0
  S.0016               R=0.0
  S.0017               V=0.0
  S.0018               X=0.0
  S.0019               WRITE(3,1000)
  S.0020          1000 FORMAT('1'4X'TIME'3X'V'6X'X'8X'R'5X'A'4X'Q'2X'U(1)'1X'U(2)'1X
                      1'U(3)'1X'U(4)'1X'U(5)'4X'C'/)
  S.0021            10 CONTINUE
  S.0022               IF(Q)40,40,20
  S.0023            20 CONTINUE
  S.0024               IF(U(1))40,40,30
  S.0025            30 U(1)=U(1)-1.0

OHIO UNIVERSITY COMPUTER CENTER FORTRAN SYSTEM

  S.0026               U(5)=U(5)+1.0
  S.0027               Q=Q-1.0
  S.0028            40 CONTINUE
  S.0029               C=C+Q*24.0/120.0
  S.0030               WRITE(3,1001) T,V,X,R,A,Q,(U(I),I=1,5),C
  S.0031          1001 FORMAT(1X,F7.1,F5.0,2F9.5,F4.0,F5.0,F4.0,4F5.0,F8.2)
  S.0032               IF(H-T/60.0)90,90,50
  S.0033            50 V=Q+U(2)+U(3)+U(4)+U(5)
  S.0034               U(1)=U(1)+U(2)
  S.0035               U(2)=U(3)
  S.0036               U(3)=U(4)
  S.0037               U(4)=U(5)
  S.0038               U(5)=0.0
  S.0039               T=T+.50
  S.0040               X=P*((S-V)/S)
  S.0041               R=RANDX(Y)
  S.0042               IF(R-X)60,70,70
  S.0043            60 CONTINUE
  S.0044               A=1.0
  S.0045               Q=Q+1.0
  S.0046               GO TO 10
  S.0047            70 A=0.0
  S.0048            80 GO TO 10
  S.0049            90 C=C+2.0*D*H
  S.0050               WRITE(3,1002) C
  S.0051          1002 FORMAT(/50X,'TOTAL COST',4X,F8.2)
  S.0052               STOP
  S.0053               END
                     SIZE OF COMMON  C0000    PROGRAM  01082
END OF COMPILATION  MAIN
```

Figure 6.4

Table 6.8

TIME	SERVED OR WAITING	ARRIVAL GREATER THAN "X"	RANDOM NUMBER	NO. ARRIVING	LGTH. OF Q	IDLE CLERKS	1/2 MIN	2/2 MIN	3/2 MIN	4/2 MIN	IDLE MACH COST
	V	X	R	A	Q	U(1)	U(2)	U(3)	U(4)	U(5)	0
0.0	0.	0.0	0.0	0.	0.	0.	0.	1.	1.	0.	0.0
0.5	2.	0.45000	0.70928	0.	0.	0.	1.	1.	0.	0.	0.0
1.0	2.	0.45000	0.74702	0.	0.	1.	1.	0.	0.	0.	0.0
1.5	1.	0.47500	0.09858	1.	0.	1.	0.	0.	0.	1.	0.0
2.0	1.	0.47500	0.86828	0.	0.	1.	0.	0.	1.	0.	C.0
2.5	1.	0.47500	0.32247	1.	0.	0.	0.	1.	0.	1.	0.0
3.0	2.	0.45000	0.12026	1.	1.	0.	1.	0.	1.	0.	0.20
3.5	3.	0.42500	0.81937	0.	0.	0.	0.	1.	0.	1.	0.20
4.0	2.	0.45000	0.83388	0.	0.	0.	1.	0.	1.	0.	0.20
4.5	2.	0.45000	0.62893	0.	0.	1.	0.	1.	0.	0.	0.20
5.0	1.	0.47500	0.26865	1.	0.	1.	0.	0.	0.	1.	0.20
5.5	2.	0.45000	0.95154	0.	0.	1.	0.	0.	1.	0.	0.20
6.0	1.	0.47500	0.29143	1.	0.	0.	0.	1.	0.	1.	0.20
6.5	2.	0.45000	0.18469	1.	1.	0.	1.	0.	1.	0.	0.40
7.0	3.	0.42500	0.48526	0.	0.	0.	0.	1.	0.	1.	0.40
7.5	2.	0.45000	0.24932	1.	1.	0.	1.	0.	1.	0.	0.60
8.0	3.	0.42500	0.12860	1.	1.	0.	0.	1.	0.	1.	0.80
8.5	3.	0.42500	0.52775	0.	1.	0.	1.	0.	1.	0.	1.00
9.0	3.	0.42500	0.00905	1.	1.	0.	0.	1.	0.	1.	1.20
9.5	3.	0.42500	0.30459	1.	2.	0.	1.	C.	1.	0.	1.60
10.0	4.	0.40000	0.74609	0.	1.	0.	0.	1.	0.	1.	1.80
10.5	3.	0.42500	0.73518	0.	1.	0.	1.	0.	1.	0.	2.00
11.0	3.	0.42500	0.69628	0.	0.	0.	0.	1.	0.	1.	2.00
11.5	2.	0.45000	0.56110	0.	0.	0.	1.	0.	1.	0.	2.00
12.0	2.	0.45000	0.10009	1.	0.	0.	0.	1.	0.	1.	2.00
12.5	2.	0.45000	0.55059	0.	0.	0.	1.	0.	1.	0.	2.00
13.0	2.	0.45000	0.40279	1.	0.	0.	0.	1.	0.	1.	2.00
13.5	2.	0.45000	0.46139	0.	0.	0.	1.	0.	1.	0.	2.00
14.0	2.	0.45000	0.14324	1.	0.	0.	0.	1.	0.	1.	2.00
14.5	2.	0.45000	0.70691	0.	0.	0.	1.	0.	1.	0.	2.00
15.0	2.	0.45000	0.95229	0.	0.	1.	0.	1.	0.	0.	2.00
15.5	1.	0.47500	0.35160	1.	0.	0.	1.	0.	0.	1.	2.00
16.0	2.	0.45000	0.53896	0.	0.	1.	0.	0.	1.	0.	2.00
16.5	1.	0.47500	0.06937	1.	0.	0.	0.	1.	0.	1.	2.00
17.0	2.	0.45000	0.56557	0.	0.	0.	1.	0.	1.	0.	2.00
17.5	2.	0.45000	0.76906	0.	0.	1.	0.	1.	0.	0.	2.00
18.0	1.	0.47500	0.52426	0.	0.	1.	1.	0.	0.	0.	2.00
18.5	1.	0.47500	0.22398	1.	0.	1.	0.	0.	0.	1.	2.00
19.0	1.	0.47500	0.62559	0.	0.	1.	0.	0.	1.	0.	2.00
19.5	1.	0.47500	0.73771	0.	0.	1.	0.	1.	0.	0.	2.00
20.0	1.	0.47500	0.79593	0.	0.	1.	1.	0.	0.	0.	2.00
20.5	1.	0.47500	0.13616	1.	0.	1.	0.	0.	0.	1.	2.00
21.0	1.	0.47500	0.65362	0.	0.	1.	0.	0.	1.	0.	2.00
21.5	1.	0.47500	0.69631	0.	0.	1.	0.	1.	0.	0.	2.00
22.0	1.	0.47500	0.29525	1.	0.	0.	1.	0.	0.	1.	2.00
22.5	2.	0.45000	0.50474	0.	0.	1.	0.	0.	1.	0.	2.00
23.0	1.	0.47500	0.37119	1.	0.	0.	0.	1.	0.	1.	2.00
23.5	2.	0.45000	0.68447	0.	0.	0.	1.	0.	1.	0.	2.00
24.0	2.	0.45000	0.76610	0.	0.	1.	0.	1.	0.	C.	2.00
24.5	1.	0.47500	0.43633	1.	0.	0.	0.	1.	0.	1.	2.00
25.0	2.	0.45000	0.72309	0.	0.	1.	0.	0.	1.	0.	2.00
25.5	1.	0.47500	0.41154	1.	0.	0.	0.	1.	0.	1.	2.00
26.0	2.	0.45000	0.96146	0.	0.	0.	1.	0.	1.	0.	2.00

TIME	SERVED OR WAITING	ARRIVAL GREATER THAN "X"	RANDOM NUMBER	NO. ARRIVING	LGTH. OF Q	IDLE CLERKS	1/2 MIN	2/2 MIN	3/2 MIN	4/2 MIN	IDLE MACH. COST
458.0*	3.	0.42500	0.65505	0.	0.	0.	0.	1.	0.	1.	151.60
458.5	2.	0.45000	0.60271	0.	0.	0.	1.	0.	1.	0.	151.60
459.0	2.	0.45000	0.72074	0.	0.	1.	0.	1.	0.	0.	151.60
459.5	1.	0.47500	0.90012	0.	0.	1.	1.	0.	0.	0.	151.60
460.0	1.	0.47500	0.91401	0.	0.	2.	0.	0.	0.	0.	151.60
460.5	0.	0.50000	0.38299	1.	0.	1.	0.	0.	0.	1.	151.60
461.0	1.	0.47500	0.07187	1.	0.	0.	0.	0.	1.	1.	151.60
461.5	2.	0.45000	0.98424	0.	0.	0.	0.	1.	1.	0.	151.60
462.0	2.	0.45000	0.25867	1.	1.	0.	1.	1.	0.	0.	151.80
462.5	3.	0.42500	0.69381	0.	0.	0.	1.	0.	0.	1.	151.80
463.0	2.	0.45000	0.83489	0.	0.	1.	0.	0.	1.	0.	151.80
463.5	1.	0.47500	0.76501	0.	0.	1.	0.	1.	0.	0.	151.80
464.0	1.	0.47500	0.07607	1.	0.	0.	1.	0.	0.	1.	151.80
464.5	2.	0.45000	0.57132	0.	0.	1.	0.	0.	1.	0.	151.80
465.0	1.	0.47500	0.74329	0.	0.	1.	0.	1.	0.	0.	151.80
465.5	1.	0.47500	0.31784	1.	0.	0.	1.	0.	0.	1.	151.80
466.0	2.	0.45000	0.21748	1.	0.	0.	0.	0.	1.	1.	151.80
466.5	2.	0.45000	0.44428	1.	1.	0.	0.	1.	1.	0.	152.00
467.0	3.	0.42500	0.7C836	0.	1.	0.	1.	1.	0.	0.	152.20
467.5	3.	0.42500	0.25164	1.	1.	0.	1.	0.	0.	1.	152.40
468.0	3.	0.42500	0.13458	1.	1.	0.	0.	0.	1.	1.	152.60
468.5	3.	0.42500	0.54276	0.	1.	0.	0.	1.	1.	0.	152.80
469.0	3.	0.42500	0.04531	1.	2.	C.	1.	1.	0.	0.	153.20
469.5	4.	0.40000	0.38699	1.	2.	0.	1.	0.	0.	1.	153.60
470.0	4.	0.40000	0.91417	0.	1.	0.	0.	0.	1.	0.	153.80
470.5	3.	0.42500	0.C0213	1.	2.	0.	0.	1.	1.	C.	154.20
471.0	4.	0.40000	0.78524	0.	2.	0.	1.	1.	0.	0.	154.60
471.5	4.	0.40000	0.69223	0.	1.	0.	1.	0.	0.	1.	154.80
472.0	3.	0.42500	0.C8624	1.	1.	C.	0.	0.	1.	1.	155.0C
472.5	3.	0.42500	0.28739	1.	2.	0.	0.	1.	1.	0.	155.40
473.0	4.	0.40000	0.94812	0.	2.	0.	1.	1.	0.	0.	155.8C
473.5	4.	0.40000	0.10228	1.	2.	0.	1.	0.	0.	1.	156.20
474.0	4.	0.40000	0.08054	1.	2.	0.	0.	0.	1.	1.	156.60
474.5	4.	0.40000	0.56276	0.	2.	0.	0.	1.	1.	0.	157.00
475.0	4.	0.40000	0.65169	0.	2.	C.	1.	1.	0.	C.	157.40
475.5	4.	0.40000	0.84529	0.	1.	0.	1.	0.	0.	1.	157.6C
476.5	3.	0.42500	0.63168	0.	1.	0.	0.	1.	1.	0.	158.C0
477.5	3.	0.42500	0.90214	0.	0.	0.	1.	0.	0.	1.	158.2C
478.5	2.	0.45000	0.07204	1.	1.	C.	0.	1.	1.	0.	158.40
479.0	3.	0.42500	0.14534	1.	2.	0.	1.	1.	0.	0.	158.80
479.5	4.	0.40000	0.22370	1.	2.	0.	1.	0.	0.	1.	159.20
480.0	4.	0.4C000	0.03417	1.	2.	0.	0.	0.	1.	1.	159.60

| | | | | | | | | | TOTAL COST | | **191.60 |

TOTAL JOB TIME FOR 10703 IS 0315.83 SECONDS

* NOTE: WE PICK UP THIS SIMULATION AT 458.0 MINUTES AND CONTINUE UNTIL CONCLUSION OF PROGRAM.
** AT THE CONCLUSION OF THIS EIGHT HOURS OF SIMULATION, THE COST FOR IDLED MACHINE WAS $159.60. THE COST FOR TWO SERVICE CLERKS WAS ($2.00)(16) = $32.00. TOTAL COSTS = $159.60 + $32.00 = $191.60.

6.44 Example IV (Station-to-Station Queue—Assignment Problem)

Case History

Aggregate, sand, cement, and other dry ingredients are fed into the central mixing unit of a batch-processing plant that is supplying concrete for a road-construction contract; these ingredients are dry-mixed here prior to the loading operation. In the final phase, these ingredients, plus water, are fed into a truck for wet-mixing while en route to the highway construction project. The maximum that one truck may carry is twelve cubic yards of concrete, owing to weight restrictions on the highway. A truck is loaded at the batch plant, travels to the road project, releases its load, returns by the same route, and then begins the cycle anew. With each load the truck route becomes longer and thus more time is spent en route to the highway project. A company can assign a total of twelve or fewer trucks to the project. This project will operate twenty-four hours a day seven days a week.

When the cement-mixer is charged, it waits at the plant until thirty revolutions are completed whereupon it begins the trip to the construction site. Each size of truck requires a different amount of time to complete its thirty revolutions. Concrete is a perishable product, especially during the hot weather, which results in a carefully-controlled number of revolutions between embarkation and destination points.[8] If the number of revolutions is less than the required tolerance limits, the truck must then complete its revolutions at the project. Too many revolutions will cause a rejected batch. When the truck load is accepted it is dumped into a form for the paving machine to spread. The batch plant can supply 500 cubic yards per hour if there are enough trucks to accept the load, but queues at both the plant and the construction site drastically reduce the number that each station can service.

In the real-world setting this is a very complex problem that requires a complete OR (Operations Research) analysis. Assume, however, that only the elemental queuing phase of the overall problem is to be investigated as a preliminary step.

Consider that an analyst has been assigned the project of establishing the correct ratio of trucks to be assigned this project. He has available three sets of four trucks with twelve, ten, and eight cubic yard capacities, respectively. For example, he may choose three twelve-yard, one ten-yard, and two eight-yard capacity trucks. His objective is to get the maximum utilization

---

[8] The revolutions at the batch-processing plant are made at a high rpm. During the trip to the construction site the revolutions are kept very low. Thus the truck should arrive at the construction site with some revolutions to spare because it will usually wait prior to entering the system. The revolutions must continue, however, to keep the concrete from setting-up.

of equipment at a minimum of cost. If he makes an incorrect assignment, cost would soar. A choice of too many trucks would result in large queues at the various processing stations, while too few would result in the highway project's being slowed; also, too few trucks would increase the idle time of the paving machine, the highway construction crew, and the batch-processing equipment with its supporting crew.

A flow-process chart of the operation shows that trucks go through numerous steps from embarkation to destination points. In the basic round trip a truck is loaded with cement, makes a trip to the construction site, releases the load, and then returns for additional concrete. But many events, one of which is waiting time, occur to make the overall trip more complex. If one truck were to be processed through every point in the entire operation it would have followed a sequence requiring many additional minutes. Consider that a truck returns to the batch-processing plant, requires minor maintenance, needs gasoline, waits in line for concrete, receives a load, waits for thirty revolutions of the drum, completes the trip, waits to unload, unloads into a form, requires cleaning by the driver, begins the return trip, is delayed because the driver stops for coffee, continues its trip and then begins a new cycle; all these given events certainly complicate an analysis and extend the total processing time.

To begin this study an analyst must first determine what historical data are readily available, whether they are reliable for this particular case, whether sampling techniques may be used for determining time values, and what type of distribution governs the various processes. In many circumstances, owing to the absence of reliable data an analyst will hypothesize the distribution to develop a model. Each size of truck has a different process time which requires a separate distribution. The trip time, however, is basically governed by traffic conditions, and thus one distribution serves all trucks regardless of size. Thus three distributions are required for "time to load truck with mixture" and for "unloading time," while one distribution is required for "minor repair or gasoline time," for "trip time," and for "personal delay time." The first set of distributions vary, while the latter group are similar regardless of truck size.

For the first analysis many samples of truck loading times were evaluated and graphed into a distribution. As in the hospital case, Chapter 4, Sec. 4.5, Table 4.3, these values were subjected to a χ^2 analysis to determine whether they followed a known distribution. Companies do not usually have a wealth of information, and when they do not the analyst must gather his own. He can do this by having each station keep records of its activities on charts that he has prepared, or he may resort to a work-sampling technique to determine the frequencies of elapsed time associated with each event.

Tables 6.9, 6.10, and 6.11 show the distribution of loading times for trucks of eight, ten, and twelve yards capacity. Through sampling techniques, the first distribution was found to be Poisson; thus, assuming the other two were similar except for their mean value, it was possible to develop them without χ^2 testing. Once these mean values were known, the data associated with the theoretical distribution were substituted, and each event was assigned a random-number range.

Such analyses as the one being presented could prove time-consuming and thus quite costly, especially in the gathering of original data. If, for example, the analyst were to gather data for a one-month period, would this be a reliable estimate of what would happen in another period? Consideration should certainly be given to the reliability of predicting for September months, based on data gathered in May. Naturally some estimate or prediction must be made otherwise no analysis would be forthcoming, since the analyst would be bogged down in the mire of trying to determine the validity of his present data. Quite frequently he may have historical data available only to find that the present sample disagrees with that of the past.

Table 6.9

LOAD TRUCK WITH CONCRETE

(Truck Capacity = Eight Cubic Yards)

$$\bar{X} = 7 \text{ min} \qquad \sigma^2 \bar{X} = 7 \text{ min} = \qquad \sigma_{\bar{X}} = \sqrt{7} \text{ min}$$

	$P(X)$	$\sum\limits_{X=X'}^{\infty} \dfrac{e^{-\lambda}\lambda^X}{X!}$	Random-Number Range
0	0.0009	1.0000	0.9999–0.9991
1	0.0064	0.9991	0.9990–0.9927
2	0.0223	0.9927	0.9926–0.9704
3	0.0521	0.9704	0.9703–0.9183
4	0.0912	0.9183	0.9182–0.8271
5	0.1277	0.8271	0.8270–0.6994
6	0.1490	0.6994	0.6993–0.5504
7	0.1490	0.5504	0.5503–0.4014
8	0.1304	0.4014	0.4013–0.2710
9	0.1014	0.2710	0.2709–0.1696
10	0.0710	0.1696	0.1695–0.0986
11	0.0452	0.0986	0.0985–0.0534
12	0.0264	0.0534	0.0533–0.0270
13	0.0142	0.0270	0.0269–0.0128
14	0.0071	0.0128	0.0127–0.0057
15	0.0033	0.0057	0.0056–0.0024
16	0.0014	0.0024	0.0023–0.0010
17	0.0006	0.0010	0.0009–0.0004
18	0.0002	0.0004	0.0003–0.0002
19	0.0001	0.0002	0.0001–0.0000

$\sum P(X) = 0.9999$

Table 6.10

LOAD TRUCK WITH CONCRETE

(Truck Capacity = Ten Cubic Yards)

$\lambda = 8$ min $\sigma = \sqrt{8}$ min

X'	$\sum\limits_{x=x'}^{\infty} \dfrac{e^{-\lambda}\lambda^{x}}{X!}$	Random-Number Range
0	1.0000	0.9999–0.9997
1	0.9997	0.9996–0.9970
2	0.9970	0.9969–0.9862
3	0.9862	0.9861–0.9576
4	0.9576	0.9575–0.9004
5	0.9004	0.9003–0.8088
6	0.8088	0.8087–0.6866
7	0.6866	0.6865–0.5470
8	0.5470	0.5469–0.4075
9	0.4075	0.4074–0.2834
10	0.2834	0.2833–0.1841
11	0.1841	0.1840–0.1119
12	0.1119	0.1118–0.0638
13	0.0638	0.0637–0.0342
14	0.0342	0.0341–0.0173
15	0.0773	0.0172–0.0082
16	0.0082	0.0081–0.0037
17	0.0037	0.0036–0.0016
18	0.0016	0.0015–0.0006
19	0.0006	0.0005–0.0003
20	0.0003	0.0002–0.0001
21	0.0001	0.0000

In such situations it is best again to sample the distribution in order to validate that which is new; but this may prove too costly and thus delay the decision-making processes.

In this case the distributions were based entirely on sampling and validating techniques such as χ^2 testing. The statistics associated with these processes were described previously in Chapter 4, Sec. 4.5, and may be reviewed in most elementary books of statistics.

Tables 6.12, 6.13, and 6.14 show the distribution for unloading times at the road-construction project. These distributions were also established by using sampling techniques similar to those associated with finding the loading-time distributions. A closer look at this total analysis will reveal this problem as a continuous or looped simulation. It differs from the previously-explained station-to-station queues in that an output from the last station returns to the first station to begin the process anew. Thus, the input–output relationship must be approximately balanced, otherwise enormous queues will build at one station and, usually, not clear. Serious problems will also arise if too many trucks are assigned this project.

Table 6.11

LOAD TRUCK WITH CONCRETE

(Truck Capacity = Twelve Cubic Yards)

	$\lambda = 9$ min	$\sigma = \sqrt{9}$ min
X'	*Cumulative Value*	*Random-Number Range*
0	1.0000	0.9999
1	0.9999	0.9998–0.9988
2	0.9988	0.9987–0.9938
3	0.9938	0.9937–0.9788
4	0.9788	0.9787–0.9450
5	0.9450	0.9449–0.8843
6	0.8843	0.8842–0.7932
7	0.7932	0.7931–0.6761
8	0.6761	0.6760–0.5443
9	0.5443	0.5442–0.4126
10	0.4126	0.4125–0.2940
11	0.2940	0.2939–0.1970
12	0.1970	0.1969–0.1242
13	0.1242	0.1241–0.0739
14	0.0739	0.0738–0.0415
15	0.0415	0.0414–0.0220
16	0.0220	0.0219–0.0111
17	0.0111	0.0110–0.0053
18	0.0053	0.0052–0.0024
19	0.0024	0.0023–0.0011
20	0.0011	0.0010–0.0005
21	0.0005	0.0004–0.0002
22	0.0002	0.0001

Tables 6.15 and 6.16 represent the distributions associated with the time to make a trip from the bulk-processing station to the road-construction project. Table 6.15 is used in this example, while Table 6.16 is for use by students in the discussion and review section. Electronic counters were placed on the truck to determine the time per trip, other procedures would have given the same information. Each trip-time varied jointly with traffic conditions and time of day. Previously-described statistical techniques were again used to show that trip-times were normally distributed; thus, theoretical values could be used to order the distinct probabilities intervals for these events along with their random-number ranges. In the beginning normalcy was assumed and a sample of truck times taken to determine the sample mean and the sample standard deviation. With this information it was possible to predict approximately how many additional samples were necessary to assure that the data would fall within desired confidence limits. In the original sample, $\bar{X} = 31$, $S = 1$, and $N = 25$. This was enough information to approximate the number of samples necessary to assure a 0.95 probability that the error of the estimate would fall within prescribed limits. During

Table 6.12

UNLOAD TRUCK AT CONSTRUCTION SITE

(Truck Capacity = Eight Cubic Yards)

$$\bar{X} = 12 \text{ min} \qquad \sigma_{\bar{X}} = \sqrt{12} \text{ min}$$

X'	Cumulative Value	Random-Number Range
0	1.0000	
1	1.0000	0.9999
2	0.9999	0.9998–0.9995
3	0.9995	0.9994–0.9977
4	0.9977	0.9976–0.9924
5	0.9924	0.9923–0.9797
6	0.9797	0.9798–0.9542
7	0.9542	0.9541–0.9105
8	0.9105	0.9104–0.8450
9	0.8450	0.8449–0.7576
10	0.7576	0.7575–0.6528
11	0.6528	0.6527–0.5384
12	0.5384	0.5383–0.4240
13	0.4240	0.4239–0.3185
14	0.3185	0.3184–0.2280
15	0.2280	0.2279–0.1556
16	0.1556	0.1555–0.1013
17	0.1013	0.1012–0.0630
18	0.0630	0.0629–0.0374
19	0.0374	0.0373–0.0213
20	0.0213	0.0212–0.0116
21	0.0116	0.0115–0.0061
22	0.0061	0.0060–0.0030
23	0.0030	0.0029–0.0015
24	0.0015	0.0014–0.0007
25	0.0007	0.0006–0.0003
26	0.0003	0.0002–0.0001
27	0.0001	0.0000

the final sampling process the analyst would continually make tests to determine when the sample size was adequate. The presample, therefore, is used only as an estimator of the actual size required, but once the final sampling is completed it too must be checked to determine whether enough total samples were taken to assure the confidence interval.[9]

Using the formula

$$n = \frac{Z_0^2 \sigma^2}{e^2}$$

[9] In the presample testing procedure, the analyst will replace σ by S, but this procedure will introduce some statistical error. He may avoid this, however, by using methods associated with small sampling techniques. Since this is merely a pretest to estimate the number of samples required, it will be acceptable to replace σ by S. Once the sampling procedure begins, a continual audit of data gathered will allow the analyst to determine n with a greater accuracy.

Table 6.13

UNLOAD TRUCK AT CONSTRUCTION SITE

(Truck Capacity = Ten Cubic Yards)

$$\lambda = 16 \text{ min} \qquad\qquad \sigma = \sqrt{16} \text{ min}$$

X'	Cumulative Value	Random-Number Range
0	1.0000	
1	1.0000	
2	1.0000	
3	1.0000	0.9999
4	0.9999	0.9998–0.9996
5	0.9996	0.9995–0.9986
6	0.9986	0.9985–0.9960
7	0.9960	0.9959–0.9900
8	0.9900	0.9899–0.9780
9	0.9780	0.9779–0.9567
10	0.9567	0.9566–0.9226
11	0.9226	0.9225–0.8730
12	0.8730	0.8729–0.8069
13	0.8069	0.8068–0.7255
14	0.7255	0.7254–0.6325
15	0.6325	0.6324–0.5333
16	0.5333	0.5332–0.4340
17	0.4340	0.4339–0.3407
18	0.3407	0.3406–0.2577
19	0.2577	0.2576–0.1878
20	0.1878	0.1877–0.1318
21	0.1318	0.1317–0.0892
22	0.0892	0.0891–0.0582
23	0.0582	0.0581–0.0367
24	0.0367	0.0366–0.0223
25	0.0223	0.0222–0.0131
26	0.0131	0.0130–0.0075
27	0.0075	0.0074–0.0041
28	0.0041	0.0040–0.0022
29	0.0022	0.0021–0.0011
30	0.0011	0.0010–0.0006
31	0.0006	0.0005–0.0003
32	0.0003	0.0002–0.0001
33	0.0001	0.0000

Where: n = number of samples required to achieve desired accuracy
Z_0 = The value of Z corresponding to desired probability
σ = Standard deviations of universe
e = Error of estimate

the analyst may get some idea how many samples he need evaluate. Pre-testing is important because it is often too costly or time-comsuming to find n, and so other procedures must be employed to determine those governing characteristics of the distribution. If, for example, n were found to equal 5,000 trips in the presample test then other mathematical techniques would be

Table 6.14

UNLOAD TRUCK AT CONSTRUCTION SITE

(Truck Capacity = Twelve Cubic Yards)

$\lambda = 20$ min $\sigma = \sqrt{20}$ min

X'	Cumulative Values	Random-Number Range
5	1.0000	0.9999
6	0.9999	0.9998–0.9997
7	0.9997	0.9996–0.9992
8	0.9992	0.9991–0.9979
9	0.9979	0.9978–0.9950
10	0.9950	0.9949–0.9829
11	0.9892	0.9891–0.9786
12	0.9786	0.9785–0.9610
13	0.9610	0.9609–0.9339
14	0.9339	0.9338–0.8951
15	0.8951	0.8950–0.8435
16	0.8435	0.8434–0.7789
17	0.7789	0.7788–0.7030
18	0.7030	0.7029–0.6186
19	0.6186	0.6185–0.5297
20	0.5297	0.5296–0.4409
21	0.4409	0.4408–0.3563
22	0.3563	0.3562–0.2794
23	0.2794	0.2793–0.2125
24	0.2125	0.2124–0.1568
25	0.1568	0.1567–0.1122
26	0.1122	0.1121–0.0779
27	0.0779	0.0778–0.0525
28	0.0525	0.0524–0.0343
29	0.0343	0.0342–0.0218
30	0.0218	0.0217–0.0135
31	0.0135	0.0134–0.0081
32	0.0081	0.0080–0.0047
33	0.0047	0.0046–0.0027
34	0.0027	0.0026–0.0015
35	0.0015	0.0014–0.0008
36	0.0008	0.0007–0.0004
37	0.0004	0.0003–0.0002
38	0.0002	0.0001–0.0000

required to solve this problem; for in this number of trips the company's phase of the project would have terminated. Under these circumstances the analyst would develop this problem using historical data, hypothetical information, or other methods. The reason he seeks reliable data is that his techniques of simulation may be statistically reliable from the standpoint of method but may also be totally unreliable because the original data were faulty.

If in the pretest, $\bar{x}$ is based on a sample, it means that it is impossible to determine $|\bar{x} - \mu|$; thus, probability language must be used to state how close $\bar{x}$ is to μ. This estimate of μ by $\bar{x}$ is subject to error, but using probability

Table 6.15

TRIP TIME TO OR FROM CONSTRUCTION SITE

(All Size Trucks)

	$\bar{x} = 30$ min	$\sigma_{\bar{x}} = 2$ min	Distance $= 7.5$ miles
Minutes per Trip	*Interval*	*Cumulative Value*	*Random-Number Range*
	−3.875	0.9999	
22.5	−3.625	0.9998	0.9999
23.0	−3.375	0.9996	0.9998–0.9997
23.5	−3.125	0.9991	0.9996–0.9992
24.0	−2.875	0.9980	0.9991–0.9981
24.5	−2.625	0.9957	0.9980–0.9958
25.0	−2.375	0.9913	0.9957–0.9914
25.5	−2.125	0.9834	0.9913–0.9835
26.0	−1.875	0.9699	0.9834–0.9700
26.5	−1.625	0.9484	0.9699–0.9485
27.0	−1.375	0.9162	0.9484–0.9163
27.5	−1.125	0.8708	0.9162–0.8709
28.0	−0.875	0.8106	0.8708–0.8107
28.5	−0.625	0.7357	0.8106–0.7358
29.0	−0.375	0.6480	0.7357–0.6481
29.5	−0.125	0.5517	0.6480–0.5518
30.0	0.125	0.4483	0.5517–0.4484
30.5	0.375	0.3520	0.4483–0.3521
31.0	0.625	0.2643	0.3520–0.2644
31.5	0.875	0.1894	0.2643–0.1895
32.0	1.125	0.1292	0.1894–0.1293
32.5	1.375	0.0838	0.1292–0.0839
33.0	1.625	0.0516	0.0838–0.0517
33.5	1.875	0.0301	0.0516–0.0302
34.0	2.125	0.0166	0.0301–0.0167
34.5	2.375	0.0087	0.0166–0.0088
35.0	2.625	0.0043	0.0087–0.0044
35.5	2.875	0.0020	0.0043–0.0021
36.0	3.125	0.0009	0.0020–0.0010
36.5	3.375	0.0004	0.0009–0.0005
37.0	3.625	0.0002	0.0004–0.0003
37.5	3.875	0.0001	0.0002

language an analyst may assess the magnitude of a predetermined or desired error. *The error of estimate, $\bar{x}$ to μ, must therefore be embodied in probability language.* For example, if he wished e to be 0.10 with a probability of 0.95 given $S = 1$, then the analyst is asking that

$$1.96\sigma_{\bar{x}} = 0.10$$

where $\sigma_{\bar{x}}$ is replaced by S.[10]

---

[10] Ninety-five percent of the central area of a normal distribution corresponds to $\pm\ 1.96$ standard deviations from μ. Values for other areas may be found in tables of areas for standard normal distributions. For example a 90% area would be equal to $\pm\ 1.64\sigma$. If the population σ were known, then $\sigma_{\bar{x}} = \sigma/\sqrt{n}$.

Continuing with this pretest analysis from the original data, it is found that

$$n = \frac{(1.96)^2(1)^2}{(0.10)^2} = \frac{3.8416}{0.0100} = 384$$

Assume that the analyst found after 200 samples that $\sigma = 2$. Then:

$$n = \frac{(1.96)^2(2)^2}{(0.10)^2} = 1537. \text{ [11]}$$

Thus the process of going from pretesting to a more extensive analysis indicates a need of more samples.[12]

Now, assuming that the analyst wished greater accuracy in his test, say $e = 0.05$ instead of $e = 0.10$; then

$$n = \frac{(1.96)^2(2)^2}{(0.05)^2} = 6148$$

which means that twice the accuracy requires four times the original number of samples.

With the completion of this pretest it was possible to develop Table 6.15, which is a theoretical normal distribution based on $\mu = 30$ and $\sigma = 2$. Knowing the parameter allowed the distribution to be divided into one-half minute intervals through the formula:

$$Z = \frac{\bar{x} - \mu}{\sigma}$$

Using mathematical tables, the interval with 28.0 as the midpoint was found:

$$Z_1 = \frac{27.75 - 30}{2} = -1.125 \quad \text{and} \quad Z_2 = \frac{28.25 - 30}{2} = -0.875$$

Using tables of areas for standard normal distribution, Z_0 to $Z_1 \approx 0.3708$ and Z_0 to $Z_2 \approx 0.3106$, therefore the interval Z_1 to Z_2, with 28.0 as a midpoint, approximately equals $(0.3708 - 0.3106) = 0.0602$. This could also be found in tables of cumulative values of areas for standard distributions. These cumulative values were used in Table 6.15 due to ease in assigning the corresponding random-number range.

[11] If $e = 0.05$ in the original formula,

$$n = \frac{(1.96)^2(1)^2}{(0.05)^2} = 1537$$

[12] In the process of doing a Monte Carlo simulation one is also dealing with sample theory. Here, too, twice the accuracy requires four times the number of samples. One may become rather adept at analysing the Monte Carlo sample; it is possible to use such techniques as the theory of runs, entropy analyses, and other statistical techniques in order to assure that the simulation is properly carried out. But again, such things as costs, time, priorities, and validity must dictate the procedures that are to be followed. Statistical reliability cannot validate an incorrect hypothesis or improper assumption with respect to the input data.

Table 6.16 is hypothesized from Table 6.15. Here the analyst assumed a distance increase from 7.5 miles to 11.25 miles with similar traffic conditions. The ratio $11.25/7.5 = 1.5$, which means that each value from the original distribution should be multiplied by 1.5. Statistically, it is known that this type of increase will result in both sigma and mu increasing similarly

Table 6.16

TRIP TIME TO OR FROM CONSTRUCTION SITE
(All Size Trucks)

	$\mu = 45$ min	$\sigma = 3$ min	Distance $= 11.25$ miles
Minutes Per Trip	Interval	Cumulative Value	Random-Number Range
	−3.417	0.9997	
35.0	−3.250	0.9994	0.9997–0.9995
35.5	−3.083	0.9990	0.9994–0.9991
36.0	−2.917	0.9983	0.9990–0.9984
36.5	−2.750	0.9970	0.9983–0.9971
37.0	−2.583	0.9951	0.9970–0.9952
37.5	−2.417	0.9922	0.9951–0.9923
38.0	−2.250	0.9878	0.9922–0.9879
38.5	−2.083	0.9812	0.9878–0.9813
39.0	−1.917	0.9726	0.9812–0.9727
39.5	−1.750	0.9599	0.9726–0.9600
40.0	−1.583	0.9429	0.9599–0.9430
40.5	−1.417	0.9222	0.9429–0.9223
41.0	−1.250	0.8944	0.9222–0.8945
41.5	−1.083	0.8599	0.8944–0.8600
42.0	−0.917	0.8212	0.8599–0.8213
42.5	−0.750	0.7734	0.8212–0.7735
43.0	−0.583	0.7190	0.7734–0.7191
43.5	−0.417	0.6628	0.7190–0.6629
44.0	−0.250	0.5987	0.6628–0.5988
44.5	−0.083	0.5319	0.5987–0.5320
45.0	0.083	0.4681	0.5319–0.4682
45.5	0.250	0.4013	0.4681–0.4014
46.0	0.417	0.3372	0.4013–0.3373
46.5	0.583	0.2810	0.3372–0.2811
47.0	0.750	0.2266	0.2810–0.2267
47.5	0.917	0.1788	0.2266–0.1789
48.0	1.083	0.1401	0.1788–0.1402
48.5	1.250	0.1056	0.1401–0.1057
49.0	1.417	0.0778	0.1056–0.0779
49.5	1.583	0.0571	0.0778–0.0572
50.0	1.750	0.0401	0.0571–0.0402
50.5	1.917	0.0274	0.0401–0.0275
51.0	2.083	0.0188	0.0274–0.0189
51.5	2.250	0.0122	0.0188–0.0123
52.0	2.417	0.0078	0.0122–0.0079
52.5	2.583	0.0049	0.0078–0.0050
53.0	2.750	0.0030	0.0049–0.0031
53.5	2.917	0.0017	0.0030–0.0018
54.0	3.083	0.0010	0.0017–0.0011
54.5	3.250	0.0006	0.0010–0.0007
55.0	3.417	0.0003	0.0006–0.0004

by one and a half. This accounts for Table 6.16 which reflects this increasing relationship when compared with Table 6.15.

Tables 6.17 and 6.18 were developed from extremely small sample sizes. The original data were gathered and the distributions hypothesized on the basis of the analyst's prior knowledge of these two events. Table 6.18 was based on a normal distribution skewed to the left. Binomial probabilities were used to establish the random-number ranges of both distributions.[13]

Simulation

To begin the actual simulation the analyst used all trucks. He soon found that large queues developed, that times were exorbitant, and that many batches of concrete were lost. Table 6.19 shows the results of this first simulation, and that queues of trucks at the construction did not clear after many trials. This experiment began with all trucks at the batch-processing station, which created large beginning queues. All other experi-

Table 6.17

MINOR REPAIR TO TRUCK OR FILL WITH GASOLINE

	$np = 10$ min	$\sqrt{npq} = 2.236$ min
X'	$\sum\limits_{X=X'}^{n} \binom{n}{X} p^X q^{n-X}$	Random-Number Range
0		
1	1.0000	
2	1.0000	0.9999–0.9998
3	0.9998	0.9997–0.9987
4	0.9987	0.9986–0.9941
5	0.9941	0.9940–0.9793
6	0.9793	0.9792–0.9423
7	0.9423	0.9422–0.8684
8	0.8684	0.8683–0.7483
9	0.7483	0.7482–0.5881
10	0.5881	0.5880–0.4119
11	0.4119	0.4118–0.2517
12	0.2517	0.2516–0.1316
13	0.1316	0.1315–0.0577
14	0.0577	0.0576–0.0207
15	0.0207	0.0206–0.0059
16	0.0059	0.0058–0.0013
17	0.0013	0.0012–0.0002
18	0.0002	0.0001–0.0000
19	0.0000	
20	0.0000	

[13] Distributions such as those associated with learning theory, transfer of heat, Bernoulian Utility, and predetermined time system—MTM—have been known to analysts for many years. Industrial engineers have also established many distributions associated with man and his machines. Thus personal time and machine distributions which are characterized by Tables 6.17 and 6.18 may be approximated from previous knowledge, once a sample is taken. Personal observations of small samples may increase the reliability owing to the analyst's knowledge, which may allow most observations to be weighted through some type of rating techniques.

Table 6.18

PERSONAL TIME—EXCLUDING FATIQUE ALLOWANCE

$$np = 5.12 \min \qquad\qquad \sqrt{npq} = 1.35 \min$$

X'	$\sum_{X=X'}^{n} \binom{n}{X} p^X q^{n-X}$	Random-Number Range
0	0.0002	0.0001–0.0002
1	0.0036	0.0003–0.0036
2	0.0253	0.0037–0.0253
3	0.1061	0.0254–0.1061
4	0.2936	0.1062–0.2936
5	0.5722	0.2937–0.5723
6	0.8309	0.5724–0.8309
7	0.9681	0.8310–0.9681
8	1.0000	0.9682–0.0000

ments began in the same way with the belief that enough iterations would result in all characteristics of the waiting line approaching a steady state. In Table 6.19 the waiting line of trucks before unloading is too large and has shown little variation; thus the combination of trucks must be changed to relieve the congestion at this area. Remember that this was an experiment to test the system and therefore did not include the sequence of all events usually experienced by a truck. This initial test showed that a change was necessary.

Reading line thirteen: a truck with eight cubic yards capacity finishes its trip at the end of 99.5 minutes, waits 1.5 minutes before being admitted to the loading area, begins loading process at 101.0 minutes and ends at 105.0 minutes, and has a compulsory wait of 10 minutes to complete the mandatory drum revolutions, beginning the trip to the construction site at 115 minutes; the trip requires 25.0 minutes, so the truck arrives at the construction site at 140.0 minutes. Here the eight yard capacity truck has passed the previously-processed twelve yard capacity truck, which means that these two have changed positions. To continue: the eight yard truck is admitted to the unloading system at 225.0 minutes after waiting 85.0 minutes, unloading time requires 10 minutes and thus the truck departs at 235.0 minutes; 3 minutes are needed to clean the truck, which results in the trip's beginning at 238.0 minutes; a trip of 28.0 minutes completes the round trip at 266.0 minutes, and the cycle begins anew.[14]

[14] Why not add "compulsory wait" and "clean trucks" to both distributions instead of carrying as a separate column? In fact, adding a number to these values only changes the position of the distribution while the standard deviation remains the same. In other problems these may be combined to simplify the process. These columns were included separately to lay out the process in its entirety. If these areas were to change, it would be easier to replace them alone rather than the total distribution. More importantly, however, this factor should be considered. In the design of this simulation it was possible for trucks to pass each other or change positions during the constant or compulsory wait-periods. Combining these would have eliminated that possibility. Also, the processing equipment is operating during the compulsory wait-time, and this would not have been shown if combined into a single distribution. Thus, in other examples it would be possible, but in this one it would distort the simulations.

From the results found in Table 6.19 it was apparent that some change in the number of trucks would be needed to reduce the queue size. This accounts for Table 6.20, which is a simulation of ten trucks with two twelve yard capacity trucks removed from the system.

Table 6.20 was developed using the same number of columns, but they were not shown because they add little to the explanation. The key column in this analysis is "truck wait," which occurs prior to the unloading operation at the road construction site. Intuitively the analyst knows that this is the column that must diminish. If the trucks wait too long their concrete will perish because of age or too many revolutions. Obviously, then, even in the absence of cost data this system needs revising; it is seen, however, that truck waiting time has diminished with this assignment of trucks, and thus an improvement has been made. The next step would be again to reduce the number of trucks for the purpose of comparison with the previous systems.

Table 6.21 is an investigation of the system with a different assignment of trucks. From the "truck wait" column it is apparent that an improvement has been made. Now that the waiting time has diminished, it becomes important to compare the waiting time of trucks and equipment; this is why the column "Equipment Waits" has been added to the analysis. This new column is a representation of how long the batch-processing equipment is idle due to an absence of trucks to service. Averaging both columns individually it is found that equipment waiting time equals 8.3 minutes and truck waiting time equals 25.9 minutes. At this point it is necessary to introduce some cost data. Consider that the batch-processing equipment costs one dollar fifty cents per minute, that the lack of concrete at the construction site costs four dollars for each minute, and that each truck costs fifty cents per minute.

If the analyst were to make a subjective evaluation at this point he would probably decide to minimize waiting time for both equipment and trucks; but recognizing the penalty associated with a construction-site queue, he would wisely choose to have some queue of trucks in conjunction with a minimum waiting time. Thus his objective for this column would be always to have a truck ready to go into the system almost at its arrival time. Recognizing the difficulty of achieving this objective, especially in lieu of the total system, he would be willing to sacrifice a queue of trucks for an absence of waiting times by the construction-site crew and machine. Continuing with his subjective analysis, he would choose to minimize the equipment waiting time column because it too has a greater cost when compared to the truck. So as the system develops the analyst will watch these columns to determine whether they are diminishing without penalizing other areas.

Table 6.21 shows that waiting time was reduced with each experiment. Thus the analyst chose to reduce the number of trucks again in an attempt to achieve a still better assignment. Here he chose to incorporate the two additional distributions accounting for personal time and delays associated

Table 6.19

Truck Capacity	Trip Ends	Truck Wait	Load Begins	RN	Time to Load Truck	Load Ends	Compulsory Wait	Trip Begins	RN	Trip Time
8		0	0	3997	8	8.0	10	18.0	2715	32.0
8		8.0	8.0	0085	11	19.0	10	29.0	0793	34.0
8		19.0	19.0	0788	9	28.0	10	38.0	9356	27.0
8		28.0	28.0	5556	6	34.0	10	44.0	2837	32.0
10		34.0	34.0	4216	8	42.0	12	54.0	1240	33.5
10		42.0	42.0	3943	9	51.0	12	63.0	4815	30.0
10		51.0	51.0	9751	3	54.0	12	66.0	3264	32.0
10		54.0	54.0	0467	13	67.0	12	79.0	5798	29.5
12		67.0	67.0	7719	7	74.0	14	88.0	6327	29.5
12		74.0	74.0	5182	9	83.0	14	97.0	4550	30.0
12		83.0	83.0	5711	8	91.0	14	105.0	6806	29.0
12		91.0	91.0	4111	10	101.0	14	115.0	9877	25.5
8	99.5	1.5	101.0	8798	4	105.0	10	115.0	9920	25.0
8	119.5	0	119.5	6367	6	125.5	10	135.5	4748	30.0
8	135.5	0	135.5	5175	7	142.5	10	152.5	4962	30.0
8	137.0	5.5	142.5	5156	7	149.5	10	159.5	6072	29.5
10	151.0	0	151.0	4671	8	159.0	12	171.0	7029	29.0
10	172.5	0	172.5	3457	9	181.5	12	193.5	1074	33.5
10	193.0	1.0	193.0	0346	13	206.0	12	218.0	1694	33.0
10	205.0	0	206.0	8176	5	211.0	12	223.0	9978	24.5
12	229.5	0	229.5	7950	6	235.5	14	249.5	5013	30.0
12	241.0	0	241.0	1151	13	254.0	14	268.0	4564	30.0
12	259.5	0	259.5	0289	15	274.5	14	288.5	1776	33.0
8	266.0	8.5	274.5	8807	4	278.5	10	288.5	6142	29.5
12	282.5	0	282.0	6792	7	289.0	14	303.0	6216	29.5
8	295.0	0	295.5	2928	8	303.5	10	313.5	3292	32.0
8	310.5	0	310.5	1986	9	319.5	10	329.5	5148	30.0

8	321.5	0	321.5	1429	10	331.5	10	341.5	4514	30.0
10	342.0	0	342.0	7741	6	348.0	12	360.0	1276	33.5
10	360.0	0	360.0	3658	9	369.0	12	379.0	1556	33.0
10	374.5	0	374.5	0778	12	386.5	12	398.5	7105	29.0
10	389.5	0	389.5	0754	12	401.5	12	413.5	4274	31.5
12	407.5	0	407.5	2202	11	418.5	14	432.5	5947	29.5
12	436.5	0	436.5	2082	11	447.5	14	463.5	1258	33.5
8	438.0	9.5	447.5	4780	7	454.5	10	464.5	0027	35.5
12	458.5	0	458.5	7673	7	465.5	14	479.5	5931	29.5
12	479.5	0	479.5	2643	11	490.5	14	504.5	5922	29.5
8	492.5	0	492.5	8257	5	497.5	10	507.5	7612	28.5
8	502.0	0	502.0	7712	5	507.0	10	517.5	0389	34.5
8	520.5	0	520.5	6171	6	526.5	10	536.5	7070	29.0
10	544.0	0	544.0	2067	10	554.0	12	566.0	1950	33.0
10	551.5	0	557.5	6255	7	564.5	12	576.5	7957	28.5
10	566.5	0	566.5	7088	6	572.5	12	584.5	7396	28.5
10	577.0	0	577.0	1587	11	588.0	12	600.0	3743	31.5
12	593.5	0	593.5	2547	11	604.5	14	618.5	3092	32.0
12	614.0	0	614.0	7629	7	621.0	14	635.0	3368	32.0
8	639.5	0	639.5	5932	6	645.5	10	655.5	8712	27.5
12	650.0	0	650.0	4728	9	659.0	14	673.0	7768	28.5
12	656.0	3.0	659.0	2688	11	670.0	14	684.0	1529	33.0
8	666.0	4.0	670.0	8567	4	674.0	10	684.0	4442	31.5
8	678.0	0	678.0	6205	6	684.0	10	694.0	2827	32.0
8	690.0	0	690.5	4719	7	697.5	10	707.5	4167	31.5
10	699.5	0	699.5	6952	6	705.5	12	717.5	4386	31.5
10	725.5	0	725.5	3892	9	734.5	12	746.5	0223	34.0
10	743.5	0	743.5	6242	7	750.5	12	762.5	5074	30.0
10	758.0	0	758.0	7642	6	764.0	12	776.0	2541	30.0
12	769.0	0	769.0	2982	11	780.0	14	794.0	2946	32.0
12	783.5	0	783.5	9410	5	788.5	14	802.5	2605	32.5
8	797.5	0	797.5	3396	8	805.5	10	815.5	7609	28.5
12	819.0	0	819.0	8141	6	825.0	14	839.0	4230	31.5

(*Continued on next facing pages*)

Table 6.19 (Continued)

Trip Ends	Truck Wait	Unload Begins	RN	Unloading Time	Unload Ends	Clean Truck	Trip Begins	RN	Trip Time
50.0	0	50.0	0304	19	69.0	3	72.0	8763	27.5
63.0	6.0	69.0	1960	25	84.0	3	87.0	2175	32.5
65.0	19.0	84.0	1045	16	100.0	3	103.0	1919	32.5
76.0	24.0	100.0	9540	7	107.0	3	110.0	9165	27.0
87.5	19.5	107.0	7915	13	120.0	4	124.0	9444	27.0
93.0	27.0	120.0	1758	20	140.0	4	144.0	7916	28.5
98.0	42.0	140.0	5743	15	155.0	4	169.0	0566	34.0
108.5	46.5	155.0	3654	17	172.0	4	176.0	6618	29.0
117.5	54.5	172.0	2312	23	195.0	5	200.0	5721	29.5
127.0	68.0	195.0	9016	14	209.0	5	214.0	9344	27.0
134.0	75.0	209.0	8092	16	225.0	5	230.0	6471	29.5
140.5	85.0	225.0	6642	10	235.0	3	238.0	8392	28.0
140.0	93.5	234.0	8120	16	250.0	5	255.0	9299	27.0
165.5	87.0	252.0	5914	11	263.0	3	269.0	9508	26.5
182.5	81.0	263.0	1186	16	279.0	3	282.0	7730	28.5
189.0	90.0	279.0	9626	6	285.0	3	288.0	1191	33.5
200.0	85.0	285.0	0355	24	309.0	4	313.0	7064	29.0
227.0	82.0	309.0	2218	19	329.0	4	333.0	9277	27.0
251.0	80.5	328.0	6375	14	342.0	4	346.0	7881	28.5
247.5	91.0	342.0	5500	15	357.0	4	361.0	7993	28.5
278.5	77.5	357.0	8197	16	373.0	5	378.0	6469	29.5
298.0	75.0	373.0	0634	27	400.0	5	405.0	4421	31.5
321.5	82.0	400.0	9236	7	407.0	3	410.0	8229	28.0
318.0	85.5	407.0	9608	13	420.0	5	425.0	0869	33.5
332.5	87.5	420.0	4582	20	440.0	5	445.0	0116	34.5
345.5	94.5	440.0	0067	21	461.0	3	464.0	7508	28.5
359.5	101.5	461.0	8659	8	467.0	3	470.0	3186	32.0

371.5	95.5	467.0	0290	19	486.0	3	489.0	4244	31.5
393.5	92.5	486.0	8340	12	498.0	4	512.0	3215	32.0
412.0	86.0	498.0	0528	23	521.0	4	525.0	1897	32.5
427.5	93.5	521.0	9680	9	530.0	4	534.0	2093	32.5
445.0	85.0	530.0	9610	9	539.0	4	543.0	0784	34.0
462.0	77.0	539.0	3864	21	560.0	5	565.0	7710	28.5
497.0	63.0	560.0	3494	22	582.0	5	587.0	9283	27.0
500.0	82.0	582.0	0881	17	599.0	3	612.0	8934	27.5
509.0	90.0	599.0	9775	12	611.0	5	616.0	0214	34.0
534.0	77.0	611.0	1821	24	617.0	5	622.0	5538	34.0
536.0	81.0	617.0	0557	18	635.0	3	638.0	8468	28.0
552.0	83.0	635.0	7000	10	645.0	3	648.0	5337	30.0
565.5	79.5	645.0	1705	15	660.0	3	663.0	8877	27.5
599.0	61.0	660.0	9778	9	669.0	4	673.0	9664	26.5
605.0	64.0	669.0	1164	21	690.0	4	694.0	3718	31.5
613.0	77.0	690.0	2634	18	708.0	4	712.0	3523	31.5
631.5	76.5	708.0	6544	14	722.0	4	726.0	3026	32.0
650.5	71.5	722.0	8721	15	737.0	5	742.0	9411	27.0
667.0	70.0	737.0	9236	14	751.0	5	756.0	8770	27.5
683.0	68.0	751.0	2305	14	765.0	3	768.0	5562	29.5
701.5	63.5	765.0	5357	19	784.0	5	789.0	4791	30.0
717.0	68.5	784.0	1385	16	800.0	3	803.0	7092	29.0
715.5	83.0	800.0	8843	15	815.0	5	820.0	5459	30.0
726.0	89.0	815.0	2116	15	830.0	3	833.0	2397	32.5
739.0	91.0	830.0	0853	17	847.0	3	850.0	3511	32.0
749.0	98.0	847.0	4975	16	863.0	4	867.0	7400	28.5
780.5	82.5	863.0	2725	18	881.0	4	885.0	2782	32.0
792.5	88.5	881.0	4628	16	897.0	4	901.0	1529	33.0
808.5	88.5	897.0	7130	14	911.0	4	915.0	3600	31.5
826.0	85.0	911.0	9404	13	924.0	5	929.0	7400	28.5
835.0	89.0	924.0	3174	22	946.0	5	951.0	4430	32.0
844.0	102.0	946.0	0939	17	953.0	3	956.0	6015	29.5
870.5	82.5	953.0	7075	17	970.0	5	975.0	8623	28.0

Table 6.20

Truck Capacity	Trip Ends	Truck Wait	Load Begins	Load Ends	Com-pulsory Wait	Trip Begins	Trip Ends	Truck Wait	Unload Begins	Unload Ends	Clean Truck	Trip Begins
8		0	0.0	8.0	10	18.0	50.0	0.0	50.0	69	3	72.0
8		8	8.0	19.0	10	29.0	63.0	6.0	69.0	84	3	87.0
8		19	19.0	28.0	10	38.0	65.0	19.0	84.0	100	3	103.0
8		28	28.0	34.0	10	44.0	76.0	24.0	100.0	107	3	110.0
10		34	34.0	42.0	12	54.0	87.5	19.5	107.0	120	4	124.0
10		42	42.0	51.0	12	63.0	93.0	27.0	120.0	140	4	144.0
10		51	51.0	54.0	12	66.0	98.0	42.0	140.0	155	4	169.0
10		54	54.0	67.0	12	79.0	108.5	46.5	155.0	172	4	176.0
12		67	67.0	74.0	14	88.0	117.5	54.5	172.0	195	5	200.0
12		74	74.0	83.0	14	97.0	127.5	68.0	195.0	209	5	214.0
8	99.5	0	99.5	103.5	10	115.0	140.0	69.0	209.0	219	3	222.0
8	119.5	0	119.5	125.5	10	135.5	165.5	53.5	219.0	230	3	233.0
8	135.5	0	135.5	142.5	10	152.5	182.5	47.5	230.0	246	3	249.0
8	137.0	5.5	142.5	149.5	10	159.5	189.0	57.0	246.0	252	3	255.0
10	151.0	0	151.0	159.0	12	171.5	200.5	51.5	252.0	276	4	280.0
10	172.5	0	172.5	181.5	12	193.5	227.0	49.0	276.0	295	4	299.0
10	193.0	0	193.0	206.0	12	218.0	251.0	47.5	295.0	309	4	313.0
10	205.0	1	206.0	211.0	12	223.0	247.5	58.0	309.0	324	4	328.0

12	229.5	0	229.5	235.5	14	249.5	279.5	44.5	324.0	340	5	345.0
12	241.0	0	241.0	254.0	14	268.0	298.0	42.0	340.0	367	5	372.0
8	250.0	4	254.0	259.0	10	269.0	298.5	68.5	367.0	380	3	383.0
8	259.5	0	259.5	267.5	10	277.5	309.5	70.5	380.0	401	3	404.0
8	277.5	0	277.5	286.5	10	296.5	326.5	74.5	401.0	409	3	412.0
8	288.5	0	288.5	298.5	10	308.5	338.5	70.5	409.0	428	3	431.0
10	309.0	0	309.0	315.0	12	327.0	360.5	67.5	428.0	440	4	444.0
10	326.0	0	326.0	335.0	12	347.0	380.0	60.0	440.0	463	4	467.0
10	335.5	0	335.5	347.5	12	359.5	388.5	74.5	463.0	472	4	476.0
10	356.5	0	356.5	368.5	12	380.5	412.0	60.0	472.0	481	5	485.0
12	374.5	0	374.5	385.5	14	399.5	429.0	52.0	481.0	502	5	507.0
12	403.5	0	403.5	412.5	14	426.5	460.0	42.0	502.0	524	5	529.0
8	415.5	0	415.5	422.5	10	432.5	468.0	56.0	524.0	541	3	544.0
8	432.5	0	432.5	437.5	10	447.5	476.0	75.0	551.0	569	3	572.0
8	444.0	0	444.0	449.0	10	459.0	493.5	65.5	559.0	569	3	572.0
8	462.5	0	462.5	468.5	10	478.5	507.5	62.0	569.0	584	3	587.0
10	476.0	0	476.0	486.0	12	498.0	531.0	53.0	584.0	593	4	597.0
10	499.5	0	499.5	506.5	12	518.5	547.0	46.0	593.0	614	4	618.0
10	508.5	0	508.5	514.5	12	526.5	535.0	59.0	614.0	632	4	636.0
10	519.0	0	519.0	530.0	12	542.0	573.5	98.5	632.0	646	4	650.0
12	535.5	0	535.5	546.5	14	560.5	592.5	53.5	646.0	661	5	666.0
12	556.0	0	556.0	563.0	14	577.0	610.0	51.0	661.0	675	5	680.0

Table 6.21

Truck Capacity	Trip Ends	Truck Wait	Load Begins	Load Ends	Equipment Waits	Compulsory Wait	Trip Begins	Trip Ends	Truck Wait	Unload Begin	Unload Ends	Clean Truck	Trip Begins
8		0	0.0	8.0	0	10	18.0	50.0	0.0	50.0	69.0	3	72.0
8		8.0	8.0	19.0	0	10	29.0	63.0	6.0	69.0	84.0	3	87.0
8		19.0	19.0	28.0	0	10	38.0	65.0	19.0	84.0	100.0	3	103.0
10		28.0	28.0	36.0	0	12	48.0	81.5	18.5	100.0	113.0	4	117.0
10		36.0	36.0	45.0	0	12	57.0	87.0	26.0	113.0	133.0	4	137.0
12		45.0	45.0	52.0	0	14	66.0	95.5	37.5	133.0	156.0	5	161.0
12		52.0	52.0	61.0	0	14	75.0	105.0	51.0	156.0	170.0	5	175.0
12		61.0	61.0	67.0	0	14	81.0	110.0	60.0	170.0	186.0	5	191.0
8	99.5	0	99.5	103.5	32.5	10	113.5	138.5	47.5	186.0	196.0	3	199.0
8	119.5	0	119.5	125.5	16.0	10	135.5	165.5	30.5	196.0	207.0	3	210.0
8	135.5	0	135.5	142.5	10.0	10	152.5	182.5	24.5	207.0	223.0	3	226.0
10	144.0	0	144.0	152.0	1.5	12	164.0	193.0	30.0	223.0	247.0	4	251.0
10	165.5	0	165.5	174.5	13.5	12	186.5	220.0	27.0	247.0	266.0	4	270.0
12	190.5	0	190.5	196.5	16.0	14	210.5	240.5	25.5	266.0	282.0	5	287.0
12	202.0	0	202.0	215.0	5.5	14	229.0	259.0	23.0	282.0	309.0	5	314.0
12	220.5	0	220.5	235.5	5.0	14	249.5	282.5	26.5	309.0	316.0	3	319.0
8	227.0	8.5	235.5	239.5	0	10	249.5	279.0	37.0	316.0	329.0	5	334.0
8	236.5	3.0	239.5	247.5	0	10	257.5	289.5	39.0	329.0	350.0	3	353.0
8	255.5	0	255.5	264.5	8.0	10	274.5	304.5	45.5	350.0	358.0	3	361.0
10	280.0	0	280.0	286.0	15.5	12	298.0	331.5	26.5	358.0	370.0	4	374.0
10	297.0	0	297.0	316.0	11.0	12	328.0	361.0	9.0	370.0	393.0	4	397.0
12	316.5	0	316.5	327.5	0.5	14	341.5	371.0	22.0	393.0	414.0	5	419.0

174

12	345.5	0	345.5	356.5	18.0	14	370.5	404.0	10.0	414.0	436.0	5	441.0
8	352.5	4.0	356.5	363.5	0	10	373.5	409.0	27.0	436.0	453.0	3	456.0
12	362.0	1.5	363.5	370.5	0	14	384.5	414.0	39.0	453.0	465.0	5	470.0
8	381.5	0	381.5	386.5	11.0	10	386.5	415.0	50.0	465.0	483.0	3	486.0
8	393.0	0	393.0	398.0	5.0	10	398.0	432.5	50.5	483.0	493.0	3	496.0
10	406.0	0	406.0	416.0	8.0	12	428.0	461.0	32.0	493.0	502.0	4	506.0
10	429.5	0	429.5	436.5	13.5	12	446.5	475.0	27.0	502.0	523.0	4	527.0
12	447.5	0	447.5	458.5	11.0	14	472.5	504.5	18.5	523.0	538.0	5	543.0
12	468.0	0	460.0	467.0	15.0	14	481.0	513.0	25.0	538.0	552.0	5	557.0
8	490.0	0	490.0	496.0	23.0	10	506.0	533.5	18.5	552.0	566.0	3	569.0
12	504.0	0	504.0	513.0	8.0	14	527.0	555.5	10.5	566.0	585.0	5	590.0
8	514.0	0	514.0	518.0	1.0	10	528.0	559.5	25.5	585.0	601.0	3	604.0
8	526.0	0	526.0	532.0	8.0	10	542.0	574.0	27.0	601.0	616.0	3	619.0
10	532.5	0	532.5	538.5	0.5	12	550.5	582.0	34.0	616.0	632.0	4	636.0
10	558.5	0	558.5	567.5	20.0	12	579.5	613.5	18.5	632.0	650.0	4	654.0
12	570.0	0	570.0	581.0	2.5	14	595.0	627.5	22.5	650.0	663.0	5	668.0
12	584.5	0	584.5	589.5	3.5	14	603.5	636.0	27.0	663.0	685.0	5	690.0
8	598.5	0	598.5	606.5	9.0	10	616.5	645.0	40.0	685.0	702.0	3	705.0
12	620.0	0	620.0	626.0	13.5	14	640.0	671.5	30.5	702.0	719.0	5	724.0
8	633.0	0	633.0	640.0	7.0	10	650.0	682.5	36.5	719.0	728.0	3	731.0
8	651.5	0	651.5	666.5	11.5	10	676.5	704.5	23.5	728.0	739.0	3	742.0
10	664.5	1.5	666.5	672.5	0	12	684.5	713.0	26.0	739.0	754.0	4	758.0
10	686.0	0	686.0	689.0	13.5	12	701.0	730.5	23.5	754.0	770.0	4	774.0
12	696.5	0	696.5	705.5	7.5	14	719.5	751.0	19.0	770.0	786.0	5	791.0
12	722.0	0	722.0	731.0	16.5	14	745.0	774.0	12.0	786.0	799.0	5	804.0
8	734.5	0	734.5	743.5	2.5	10	753.5	781.5	17.5	799.0	814.0	3	817.0

(Continued on next pages)

Table 6.21 (Continued)

Truck Capacity	Trip Ends	Truck Wait	Load Begins	Load Ends	Equipment Waits	Compulsory Wait	Trip Begins	Trip Ends	Truck Wait	Unload Begins	Unload Ends	Clean Truck	Trip Begins
12	752.0	0	752.0	757.0	8.5	14	771.0	800.0	14.0	814.0	830.0	5	835.0
8	761.0	0	761.0	769.0	4.0	10	779.0	806.5	23.5	830.0	843.0	3	846.0
8	773.5	0	773.5	777.5	4.5	10	787.5	816.5	26.5	843.0	855.0	3	858.0
10	788.0	0	788.0	799.0	10.5	12	811.0	843.4	11.5	855.0	870.0	4	874.0
10	808.0	0	808.0	814.0	9.0	12	816.0	845.5	24.5	870.0	883.0	4	887.0
12	819.0	0	819.0	835.0	5.0	14	849.0	877.0	6.0	883.0	901.0	5	906.0
12	833.5	1.5	835.0	844.0	0	14	858.0	888.0	13.0	901.0	919.0	5	924.0
8	841.0	3.0	844.0	853.0	0	10	863.0	891.5	27.5	919.0	932.0	3	935.0
12	865.0	0	865.0	877.0	12.0	14	891.0	919.0	13.0	932.0	944.0	5	949.0
8	878.5	0	878.5	891.5	1.5	10	901.5	934.0	10.0	944.0	962.0	3	965.0
8	889.5	2.0	891.5	899.5	0	10	909.5	935.5	26.5	962.0	971.0	3	974.0
10	902.0	0	902.0	914.0	2.5	12	926.0	956.0	15.0	971.0	982.0	4	986.0
10	916.0	0	916.0	928.0	2.0	12	940.0	971.5	10.5	982.0	996.0	4	1000.0
12	936.0	0	936.0	946.0	8.0	14	960.0	989.5	6.5	996.0	1011.0	5	1016.0
12	952.0	0	952.0	964.0	6.0	14	978.0	1005.0	6.0	1011.0	1033.0	5	1038.0
8	966.5	0	966.5	970.5	2.5	10	980.5	1010.0	23.0	1033.0	1044.0	3	1047.0
12	979.5	0	979.5	985.5	9.0	14	999.5	1028.0	16.0	1044.0	1062.0	5	1067.0
8	996.5	0	996.5	1001.5	11.0	10	1011.5	1040.5	21.5	1062.0	1076.0	3	1079.0
8	1002.0	0	1002.0	1011.0	0.5	10	1021.0	1049.5	26.5	1076.0	1092.0	3	1095.0
10	1020.0	0	1020.0	1027.0	9.0	12	1039.0	1067.5	24.5	1092.0	1108.0	4	1112.0
10	1033.5	0	1033.5	1044.5	6.5	12	1056.5	1089.0	19.0	1108.0	1126.0	4	1130.0
12	1049.5	0	1049.5	1054.5	5.0	14	1068.5	1102.5	23.5	1126.0	1145.0	5	1150.0

12	1073.0	0	1073.0	1076.0	18.5	14	1090.0	1118.5	26.5	1145.0	1171.0	5	1176.0
8	1080.0	0	1080.0	1087.0	4.0	10	1097.0	1126.0	45.0	1171.0	1185.0	3	1188.0
12	1094.0	0	1094.0	1100.0	7.0	14	1114.0	1144.0	40.0	1185.0	1210.0	5	1215.0
8	1111.5	0	1111.5	1115.5	11.5	10	1125.5	1159.0	51.0	1210.0	1222.0	3	1225.0
8	1129.0	0	1129.0	1137.0	13.5	10	1137.0	1170.0	52.0	1222.0	1229.0	3	1232.0
10	1139.0	0	1139.0	1147.0	2.0	12	1159.0	1192.0	37.0	1229.0	1249.0	4	1253.0
10	1157.0	0	1157.0	1169.0	10.0	12	1181.0	1213.0	36.0	1249.0	1264.0	4	1268.0
12	1184.0	0	1184.0	1195.0	15.0	14	1209.0	1241.0	23.0	1264.0	1285.0	5	1290.0
12	1208.5	0	1208.5	1214.0	13.0	14	1228.0	1261.5	23.5	1285.0	1307.0	5	1312.0
8	1220.5	0	1220.5	1228.5	6.5	10	1238.5	1270.0	37.0	1307.0	1318.0	3	1321.0
12	1242.0	0	1242.0	1256.0	13.5	14	1270.0	1302.5	16.0	1318.0	1334.0	5	1339.0
8	1253.0	3.0	1256.0	1265.0	0	10	1275.0	1308.5	26.0	1334.0	1352.0	3	1355.0
8	1265.5	0	1265.5	1274.5	0.5	10	1284.5	1316.0	36.0	1352.0	1362.0	3	1365.0
10	1280.5	0	1280.5	1286.5	6.0	12	1298.5	1332.5	29.5	1362.0	1374.0	4	1378.0
10	1297.0	0	1297.0	1305.0	10.5	12	1317.0	1345.5	28.5	1374.0	1389.0	4	1393.0
12	1321.5	0	1321.0	1328.0	16.0	14	1342.0	1372.0	17.0	1389.0	1411.0	5	1416.0
12	1344.5	0	1344.0	1352.0	16.0	14	1366.0	1394.5	16.5	1411.0	1428.0	5	1433.0
8	1354.5	0	1354.5	1358.5	2.5	10	1368.5	1395.5	32.5	1428.0	1442.0	3	1445.0
12	1371.5	0	1371.5	1379.5	13.0	14	1393.5	1421.5	20.5	1442.0	1462.0	5	1466.0
8	1388.0	0	1388.0	1392.5	8.5	10	1402.5	1432.0	29.0	1461.0	1474.0	3	1477.0
8	1397.0	0	1397.0	1400.0	4.5	10	1410.0	1436.0	38.0	1474.0	1487.0	3	1490.0
10	1407.0	0	1407.0	1411.0	7.0	12	1423.0	1455.0	32.0	1487.0	1504.0	4	1508.0
10	1422.5	0	1422.5	1430.5	11.5	12	1442.5	1474.5	29.5	1504.0	1517.0	4	1521.0
10	1444.5	0	1444.5	1455.5	14.0	14	1469.5	1498.5	18.5	1517.0	1532.0	5	1531.0
12	1465.0	0	1465.0	1473.0	9.5	14	1487.0	1518.5	13.5	1532.0	1548.0	5	1553.0
8	1477.0	0	1477.0	1482.0	4.0	10	1492.0	1521.5	27.0	1548.0	1555.0	3	1558.0

Table 6.22

Truck Capacity	Trip Ends	RN	Delay to Service Truck	RN	Length of Delay	Truck Wait	Load Begins	RN
8		97	No	0670	0	0	0	8093
8		18	Yes	9220	7	5	5	8454
8		30	No	9317	0	9	9	0448
10		29	No	0278	0	21	21	7210
12		55	No	2581	0	27	27	9270
12		74	No	9474	0	32	32	6591
12		57	No	2742	0	40	40	2903
						$\bar{x}_1 = 19.1$		
8	102.0	26	No	1051	0	0	102.0	3426
8	110.5	55	No	5564	0	0	110.5	5286
8	122.0	18	Yes	2760	11	0	133.0	6804
10	142.0	75	No	5142	0	0	142.0	9106
12	168.5	00	Yes	1484	12	0	180.5	8648
12	192.0	97	No	2921	0	0	192.0	4941
12	216.0	34	No	6439	0	0	216.0	8817
						$\bar{x}_2 = 0$		
8	→ 219.5	08	Yes	7802	8	0	227.5	8211
8	233.5	99	No	0827	0	0	233.5	5089
8	241.5	30	No	2023	0	0	241.5	1861
10	249.5	91	No	7548	0	1.0	250.5	2448
12	284.0	64	No	7780	0	0	284.0	2157
12	303.5	77	No	6580	0	0	303.5	5877
12	321.0	81	No	7410	0	0	321.5	0881
						$\bar{x}_3 = 0.1$		
8	327.5	69	No	9868	0	7.0	334.5	0673
8	342.5	21	Yes	9283	7	0	349.5	1713
8	355.5	29	No	1164	0	3.0	358.5	7124
10	375.0	92	No	5828	0	0	375.0	2579
12	388.0	16	Yes	2167	12	0	400.0	5384
12	404.0	82	No	7927	0	5.0	409.0	2147
12	428.0	28	No	8692	0	0	428.0	9348
						$\bar{x}_4 = 2.1$		
8	431.5	58	No	4212	0	1.5	433.0	7103
8	448.5	78	No	4698	0	0	448.5	7848
8	462.5	54	No	9934	0	0	462.5	0935
10	485.0	02	Yes	8816	7	0	492.0	8978
12	506.0	82	No	2771	0	0	506.0	8805
12	531.0	80	No	0648	0	0	531.0	7797
12	560.5	73	No	1913	0	0	560.5	9344
						$\bar{x}_5 = 0.2$		

Time to Load Truck	Load Ends	Equipment Waits	Compulsory Wait	Trip Begins	RN	Trip Time	Trip Ends
5	5	0	10	15	1044	33.5	48.5
4	9	0	10	19	6031	29.5	48.5
12	21	0	10	31	7311	29.0	60.0
6	27	0	12	39	2335	32.5	71.5
5	32	0	14	46	1142	33.5	79.5
8	40	0	14	54	5921	29.5	83.5
11	51	0	14	65	7613	28.5	93.5
		$\bar{x}_1 = 0$					
8	110.0	51.0	10	120.0	6897	29.0	149.0
7	117.5	0.5	10	127.5	7618	28.5	156.0
6	139.0	15.5	10	149.0	0630	34.0	183.0
4	146.0	13.0	12	158.0	1629	33.0	191.0
6	186.5	34.5	14	200.5	8555	28.0	228.5
10	202.0	5.5	14	216.0	5974	29.5	245.5
6	222.0	14.0	14	236.0	4157	31.5	267.5
		$\bar{x}_2 = 17.7$					
5	232.5	5.5	10	242.5	5538	29.5	272.0
7	240.5	1.0	10	250.5	4904	30.0	280.5
9	250.5	1.0	10	260.5	3149	32.0	292.5
10	260.5	0	12	272.5	3032	32.0	304.5
11	295.0	23.5	14	309.0	1645	33.0	342.0
8	311.5	8.5	14	320.0	8156	38.0	358.0
13	334.5	10.0	14	344.5	6255	29.5	374.0
		$\bar{x}_3 = 7.1$					
11	345.5	0	10	355.5	4660	30.0	385.5
9	358.5	11.0	10	368.5	9480	27.0	395.5
5	363.5	0	10	373.5	5479	30.0	403.5
10	385.0	11.5	12	397.0	6297	29.5	426.5
9	409.0	15.0	14	423.0	9327	27.0	450.0
11	420.0	0	14	434.0	7284	29.0	463.0
5	433.0	8.0	14	447.0	6886	29.0	476.0
		$\bar{x}_4 = 6.5$					
5	438.0	0	10	448.0	3894	31.5	479.5
5	453.5	10.5	10	463.5	0709	34.0	497.5
11	473.5	9.0	10	483.5	9505	26.5	510.0
5	497.0	18.5	12	509.0	9579	26.5	535.5
6	512.0	9.0	14	526.0	3962	31.5	557.5
7	538.0	19.0	14	552.0	7438	28.5	580.5
5	565.5	21.5	14	579.5	0925	33.5	613.0
		$\bar{x}_5 = 12.5$					

(*Continued on next facing pages*)

Tableau 6.22 (Continued)

Truck Capacity	Trip Ends	RN	Delay to Service Truck	RN	Length of Delay	Truck Wait	Load Begins	RN
8	562.0	92	No	5083	0	3.5	565.5	1258
8	566.0	48	No	2993	0	9.5	575.5	5675
8	585.0	14	Yes	6083	9	0	593.0	9459
10	608.0	76	No	2363	0	0	608.0	5960
12	626.5	56	No	6344	0	0	626.5	1699
12	647.5	05	Yes	1972	12	0	659.5	4359
12	668.0	74	No	5006	0	0.5	668.5	6526

$$\bar{x}_6 = 1.9$$

8	676.5	58	No	2188	0	0	676.5	2971
8	695.0	27	No	3550	0	0	695.0	0702
8	706.5	31	No	6268	0	0	706.5	8779
10	729.0	22	Yes	1860	12	0	741.0	0579
12	752.0	67	No	9144	0	2.0	754.0	3581
12	765.0	86	No	1205	0	0	765.0	7524
12	792.0	14	Yes	1429	12	0	804.0	6097

$$\bar{x}_7 = 0.3$$

8	792.5	42	No	5644	0	19.5	812.0	7786
8	803.0	76	No	0136	0	14.5	817.5	5095
8	811.5	64	No	9784	0	13.0	824.5	8510
10	849.5	13	Yes	6943	9	0	858.5	6057
12	887.5	78	No	0747	0	0	887.5	0394
12	901.5	94	No	0292	0	1.0	902.5	8985
12	930.5	74	No	0721	0	0	930.5	9916

$$\bar{x}_8 = 6.9$$

8	937.5	72	No	7484	0	0	937.5	3122
8	944.5	62	No	9203	0	1.0	945.5	2600
8	956.5	48	No	0975	0	0	956.5	5013
10	971.5	20	Yes	5392	10	0	981.5	4043
12	993.0	97	No	3376	0	0	993.0	9699
12	1014.5	39	No	2995	0	0	1014.5	9468
12	1036.0	37	No	0204	0	0	1036.0	3699

$$\bar{x}_9 = 0.1$$

8	1040.0	20	Yes	4213	10	0	1050.0	4260
8	1050.5	23	No	5441	0	6.5	1057.0	9095
8	1064.5	85	No	5307	0	0	1064.5	7707
10	1097.5	21	Yes	1581	12	0	1109.5	1951
12	1116.0	44	No	9978	0	3.5	1119.5	1794
12	1128.0	30	No	3587	0	3.5	1131.5	3652
12	→ 1158.5	58	No	2195	0	0	1158.5	5159

$$\bar{x}_{10} = 1.9$$

$$\frac{1}{n} \sum_{i=3}^{10} x_i = \bar{\bar{x}}$$
$$= 1.7$$

Time to Load Truck	Load Ends	Equipment Waits	Compulsory Wait	Trip Begins	RN	Trip Time	Trip Ends
10	575.5	0	10	585.5	7120	29.0	614.5
6	581.5	0	10	591.5	3857	31.5	622.5
3	596.0	11.5	10	606.0	3575	31.5	637.5
7	615.0	12.0	12	627.0	3055	32.0	659.0
12	628.5	11.5	14	642.5	2361	32.5	675.0
9	668.5	31.0	14	682.5	7212	29.0	711.5
8	676.5	0	14	690.5	5448	30.0	720.5

$$\bar{x}_6 = 9.4$$

Time to Load Truck	Load Ends	Equipment Waits	Compulsory Wait	Trip Begins	RN	Trip Time	Trip Ends
8	684.5	0	10	694.5	1646	33.0	727.5
11	706.0	10.5	10	716.0	7787	28.5	744.5
4	710.5	0.5	10	720.5	7058	29.0	749.5
13	754.0	20.5	12	766.0	0002	37.5	803.5
10	764.0	0	14	778.0	5578	29.5	807.5
7	772.0	1.0	14	786.0	4422	31.5	817.5
8	812.0	32.0	14	826.0	5920	29.5	855.5

$$\bar{x}_7 = 9.2$$

Time to Load Truck	Load Ends	Equipment Waits	Compulsory Wait	Trip Begins	RN	Trip Time	Trip Ends
5	817.5	0	10	827.5	8092	28.5	856.0
7	824.5	0	10	834.5	2510	32.5	867.0
4	828.5	0	10	838.5	0570	34.0	872.5
7	865.5	30.0	12	877.5	0541	34.0	911.5
15	902.5	22.0	14	916.5	7871	28.5	945.0
5	907.5	0	14	921.5	0479	34.5	956.0
3	933.5	23.0	14	947.5	3242	32.0	979.5

$$\bar{x}_8 = 10.7$$

Time to Load Truck	Load Ends	Equipment Waits	Compulsory Wait	Trip Begins	RN	Trip Time	Trip Ends
8	945.5	4.0	10	955.5	0163	34.5	990.0
9	954.5	0	10	964.5	1435	34.5	999.0
7	963.5	2.0	10	973.5	8090	28.5	1002.0
9	990.5	18.0	12	1002.5	3241	32.0	1034.5
4	997.0	2.5	14	1011.0	8067	28.5	1039.5
4	1018.5	17.5	14	1032.5	7442	28.5	1061.0
10	1046.0	17.5	14	1060.0	2184	32.5	1092.5

$$\bar{x}_9 = 8.8$$

Time to Load Truck	Load Ends	Equipment Waits	Compulsory Wait	Trip Begins	RN	Trip Time	Trip Ends
7	1057.0	4.0	10	1067.0	7215	29.0	1096.0
7	1064.0	0	10	1074.0	4627	30.0	1104.0
7	1071.5	0.5	10	1081.5	2774	32.0	1113.5
10	1119.5	38.0	12	1131.5	4271	31.5	1163.0
12	1131.5	0	14	1145.5	5299	30.0	1175.5
10	1141.5	0	14	1155.5	1586	33.0	1188.5
9	1167.5	17.0	14	1181.5	3148	32.0	1213.5

$$\bar{x}_{10} = 8.5$$

$$\frac{1}{n} \sum_{i=3}^{10} x_i = \bar{\bar{x}}$$
$$= 9.1$$

(*Continued on next facing pages*)

Tableau 6.22 (Continued)

Truck Waits	Unload Begins	RN	Un- loading Time	Unload Ends	Paver Waits	Clean Truck	Trip Begins
0	48.5	6785	10	58.5	48.5	3	61.5
10	58.5	2184	15	73.5	0	3	76.5
13.5	73.5	0824	17	90.5	0	3	93.5
19.0	90.5	6423	15	105.5	0	4	109.5
26.0	105.5	2166	23	128.5	0	5	133.5
45.0	128.5	4317	21	149.5	0	5	154.5
56.0	149.5	4746	20	169.5	0	5	174.5
$\bar{x}_1 = 24.2$					$\bar{x}_1 = 6.9$		
20.5	169.5	7892	9	178.5	0	3	181.5
22.5	178.5	0045	22	200.5	0	3	203.5
17.5	200.5	9696	6	206.5	0	3	209.5
15.5	206.5	9766	9	215.5	0	4	219.5
0	228.5	6700	18	246.5	13.0	5	251.5
1.0	246.5	2018	24	270.5	0	5	275.5
3.0	270.5	8862	15	285.5	0	5	290.0
$\bar{x}_2 = 11.4$					$\bar{x}_2 = 1.9$		
13.5	285.5	8037	9	294.5	0	3	297.5
14.0	294.5	3407	13	307.5	0	3	310.5
15.0	307.5	6208	11	318.5	0	3	321.5
14.0	318.5	5035	16	334.5	0	4	338.5
0	342.0	9774	12	354.0	7.5	5	359.0
0	358.0	4970	9	367.0	4.0	5	372.0
0	374.0	8576	15	389.0	7.0	5	394.0
$\bar{x}_3 = 8.1$					$\bar{x}_3 = 2.6$		
3.5	389.0	6433	11	400.0	0	3	403.0
4.5	400.0	2745	14	414.0	0	3	417.0
10.5	414.0	3622	13	427.0	0	3	430.0
0.5	427.0	4339	17	444.0	0	4	448.0
0	450.0	3020	22	472.0	6.0	5	477.0
9.2	472.0	0922	26	498.0	0	5	503.0
22.0	498.0	3853	21	519.0	0	5	524.0
$\bar{x}_4 = 7.1$					$\bar{x}_4 = 0.9$		
39.5	519.0	8814	8	527.0	0	3	530.0
29.5	527.0	9332	7	534.0	0	3	537.0
24.0	534.0	5871	11	545.0	0	3	548.0
9.5	545.0	1103	21	566.0	0	4	570.0
8.5	566.0	2625	23	589.0	0	5	594.0
8.5	589.0	5065	20	609.0	0	5	614.0
0	613.0	9938	10	623.0	4.0	5	628.0
$\bar{x}_5 = 17.1$					$\bar{x}_5 = 0.6$		

RN	Personal Delay?	RN	Length of Delay	RN	Trip Time	Age of Concrete	Time in System
25	Yes	5743	6	0510	34.5	43.5	102.0
02	Yes	3654	5	6580	29.0	49.5	110.5
82	No	2312	0	7845	28.5	52.5	122.0
50	No	9016	0	2428	32.5	63.5	142.0
17	Yes	8092	6	7205	29.0	73.5	168.5
06	Yes	6642	6	3646	31.5	88.5	192.0
39	Yes	8763	7	0103	34.5	98.5	216.0
						$\bar{x}_1 = 67.1$	
04	Yes	2652	4	0575	34.0	59.5	117.5
77	No	7422	0	5144	30.0	61.0	123.0
60	No	5297	0	3387	32.0	61.5	119.5
45	No	5070	0	5348	30.0	60.5	107.5
06	Yes	8787	7	9856	25.5	42.0	115.5
50	No	0057	0	8110	28.0	44.5	111.5
40	Yes	0358	3	8338	28.0	48.5	105.0
						$\bar{x}_2 = 53.9$	
59	No	8114	0	4486	30.0	53.0	108.0
90	No	9233	0	3092	32.0	54.0	109.0
42	No	2731	0	0892	33.5	57.0	114.0
28	Yes	8603	7	6216	29.5	58.0	125.5
80	No	6104	0	5933	29.0	47.0	104.0
10	Yes	6503	6	9764	26.0	46.5	100.5
64	No	8620	0	0837	34.0	39.5	107.0
						$\bar{x}_3 = 50.7$	
81	No	3340	0	7598	28.5	43.5	104.0
75	No	5803	0	3823	31.5	41.5	106.0
21	Yes	5268	5	9014	27.5	50.5	107.0
08	Yes	5382	5	3233	32.0	42.0	110.0
86	No	1014	0	6489	29.0	41.0	118.0
44	No	5323	0	8572	28.0	52.0	127.0
15	Yes	8648	7	5917	29.5	65.0	132.0
						$\bar{x}_4 = 47.9$	
46	No	4857	0	2719	32.0	81.0	130.5
69	No	0591	0	6781	29.0	73.5	117.5
04	Yes	4661	5	2905	32.0	60.5	122.5
01	Yes	6271	6	1955	32.5	48.0	123.5
60	No	7678	0	2190	32.5	54.0	120.5
12	Yes	5290	5	7749	28.5	51.0	116.5
16	Yes	7301	6	0244	34.0	47.5	107.5
						$\bar{x}_5 = 59.4$	

(Continued on next facing pages)

Tableau 6.22 (Continued)

Truck Waits	Unload Begins	RN	Un- loading Time	Unload Ends	Paver Waits	Clean Truck	Trip Begins
8.5	623.0	0369	19	642.0	0	3	645.0
19.5	642.0	2903	14	656.0	0	3	659.0
18.5	656.0	1632	16	672.0	0	3	675.0
13.0	672.0	1558	20	692.0	0	4	696.0
17.0	692.0	1441	25	717.0	0	5	722.0
5.5	717.0	8439	15	732.0	0	5	737.0
11.5	732.0	4688	20	752.0	0	5	757.0
$\bar{x}_6 = 13.4$					$\bar{x}_6 = 0$		
0	752.0	8774	8	760.0	0	3	763.0
15.5	760.0	6643	10	770.0	0	3	773.0
20.5	770.0	7181	10	780.0	0	3	783.0
0	803.5	5234	16	819.5	23.5	4	823.5
12.0	819.5	0269	29	848.5	0	5	853.5
31.0	848.5	4116	21	869.5	0	5	874.5
14.0	869.5	7700	17	886.5	0	5	891.5
$\bar{x}_7 = 13.3$					$\bar{x}_7 = 3.4$		
30.5	886.5	7941	9	895.5	0	3	898.5
28.5	895.5	0922	17	912.5	0	3	915.5
40.0	912.5	4599	12	924.5	0	3	927.5
13.0	924.5	3979	17	941.5	0	4	945.5
0	945.0	8922	15	960.0	3.5	5	965.0
14.0	960.0	9525	13	973.0	0.5	5	978.0
0	979.5	7195	17	996.5	6.5	5	1001.5
$\bar{x}_8 = 18.0$					$\bar{x}_8 = 1.4$		
6.5	996.5	5675	11	1007.5	0	3	1010.5
8.5	1007.5	4002	13	1020.5	0	3	1023.5
18.5	1020.5	6230	11	1031.5	0	3	1034.5
0	1034.5	0154	25	1059.5	3.0	4	1063.5
20.0	1059.5	4302	16	1075.5	0	5	1080.5
14.5	1075.5	4001	16	1091.5	0	5	1096.5
0	1092.5	6008	19	1111.5	1.0	5	1116.5
$\bar{x}_9 = 9.7$					$\bar{x}_9 = 0.6$		
15.5	1111.5	4002	13	1124.5	0	3	1127.5
20.5	1124.5	5112	12	1136.5	0	3	1139.5
23.0	1136.5	6016	11	1147.5	0	3	1150.5
0	1163.0	8228	12	1175.0	15.5	4	1179.0
0	1175.5	1002	24	1199.5	0.5	5	1204.5
11.0	1199.5	7366	17	1216.5	0	5	1221.5
3.0	1216.5	3947	21	1237.5	0	5	1242.5
$\bar{x}_{10} = 10.4$					$\bar{x}_{10} = 2.3$		
$\bar{\bar{x}} = 12.1$							

$$\frac{1}{n} \sum_{i=6}^{10} \bar{x}_i = \bar{\bar{x}}$$
$$= 1.5$$

RN	Personal Delay?	RN	Length of Delay	RN	Trip Time	Age of Concrete	Time in System
98	No	3136	0	3561	31.5	47.5	114.5
39	Yes	1836	4	3489	32.0	60.5	129.0
05	Yes	8838	7	9971	24.5	60.0	121.5
51	No	9233	0	1307	33.0	57.0	120.5
59	No	7877	0	4879	30.0	63.5	125.5
78	No	1802	0	8348	28.0	48.5	117.5
04	Yes	8041	6	6611	29.0	55.5	124.0
						$\bar{x}_6 = 56.1$	
52	No	7688	0	5857	29.5	67.5	116.0
58	No	6121	0	5014	30.0	54.0	108.0
57	No	8859	0	7943	28.5	59.5	105.0
87	No	2256	0	9714	26.0	49.5	120.5
70	No	9174	0	0759	34.0	55.5	135.5
97	No	5183	0	9390	27.0	76.5	136.5
22	Yes	6794	6	1749	33.0	57.5	138.5
						$\bar{x}_7 = 60.0$	
35	Yes	7971	6	1308	33.0	69.0	145.0
69	No	7075	0	7285	29.0	71.0	141.5
96	No	0939	0	7252	29.0	84.0	145.0
45	No	3174	0	9759	26.0	59.0	122.0
67	No	3242	0	8534	28.0	42.5	105.5
25	Yes	0784	3	1164	33.5	52.5	113.0
34	Yes	0658	3	4413	31.5	46.0	105.5
						$\bar{x}_8 = 60.6$	
80	No	9938	0	6052	29.5	51.0	102.5
97	No	2036	0	9467	27.0	53.0	106.0
93	No	4290	0	5417	30.0	57.0	108.0
84	No	0163	0	0740	34.0	44.0	126.0
10	Yes	7155	3	2239	32.5	62.5	123.0
83	No	1141	0	3869	31.5	57.0	113.5
42	Yes	9856	8	0269	34.0	46.5	122.5
						$\bar{x}_9 = 53.0$	
38	Yes	4442	3	8276	28.0	54.5	118.5
57	No	0557	0	9139	27.5	60.5	116.5
12	Yes	7000	3	1411	33.0	65.0	122.0
71	No	7612	0	3961	31.5	43.5	113.0
67	No	0394	0	4104	31.5	44.0	120.0
55	No	7070	0	9827	26.0	58.0	119.5
88	No	1950	0	6724	29.0 (1271.5)	49.0	113.0
						$\bar{x}_{10} = 53.5$	
						$\bar{\bar{x}} = 55.2$	$\bar{x} = 118.3$

with truck servicing time; now the system could be evaluated in its entirety.[15]

Table 6.22 is the final simulation given in this example. In fact, other assignments may prove to be better; this is left for student evaluation as a Discussion and Review Problem in Sec. 6.5. In this final table all columns are included along with the random numbers used to generate the analysis. A previous study showed that twenty-two percent of the time a truck cycle was extended due to minor repairs or gasoline needs. Similarly, personal delays occurred forty percent of the time. Returning to Table 6.22, it may be seen that an improvement was made over the previous systems because truck waiting time was reduced prior to the paving operation—previously described as work at the construction site. Before beginning the final analysis of this table, it would be wise first to read one line. Taking it at the row reading 1040.0 minutes for an eight yard capacity truck, it reads: an eight yard capacity truck returns to the batch-processing plant with its trip ending at 1040.0 minutes, random number $20 \leq 22$, which indicates that a truck will stop for minor repairs or gasoline; now that a delay has occurred, it will be necessary to determine its length. Table 6.17 is used for this purpose, and it is found that minor repairs lasting ten minutes are required before entering the loading system. The truck enters the loading system at 1050.0 minutes and does not wait, since the previous truck had cleared at 1046.0 minutes; loading time was 7.0 minutes, and the batch-processing equipment waited $(1050.0 - 1046.0) = 4.0$ minutes. Further: after a compulsory wait of ten minutes the trip begins at 1067.0 minutes and ends at 1096.0 minutes. The total trip time being 29.0 minutes, unloading cannot begin until 1111.5 minutes because the previous truck has not finished, thus the incoming truck must wait $(1111.5 - 1096.0) = 15.5$ minutes. With an unloading time of 13 minutes, the truck has cleared the paving operation at 1124.5 minutes, but the paving machine had $(1111.5 - 1111.5) = 0$ minutes waiting time. After a cleaning operation of 3 minutes, the truck begins its return trip at 1127.5 minutes. A personal delay occurs in this cycle as random numbers $38 \leq 40$, personal time requires 3 minutes, and the trip requires a total of 28.0 minutes for completion. The age of the concrete before it was unloaded is $(1111.5 - 1057.0) = 54.5$ minutes, and the total time for the truck to make a complete trip was $[(1127.5 + 3 + 28.0) - 1040.0] = 118.5$ minutes.

Only ten cycles of this final problem were developed, but it still yields valuable information. The average waiting times for the last eight cycles

[15] Remember that every experiment was a test to determine whether the simulation was approaching a state where overall costs were minimized. Making these experiments in the absence of a computer will soon teach the analyst not to investigate the total system until the previous experiment warrants it. This also holds true when using a computer. Why take valuable computer time in the initial experiments? There is a correct analyst-to-programmer-to-computer ratio, but this is sometimes overlooked. Analysis of subsystems has merit even when a computer is being used.

were: 1.7 minutes truck waits before loading; 9.1 minutes batch-processing plant waits for truck; 12.1 minutes truck waits before unloading; 1.5 minutes paver waits for trucks; 55.2 minutes the average age of concrete; and 118.3 minutes the truck time in the system. To analyze this problem further, assume that the concrete will be discarded if it has aged more than eighty-five minutes prior to the unloading operation. From Table 6.22 it may be seen there are no such occurrences. The first two cycles involving two complete trips for each of the trucks were not used because the system had not been operating long enough to minimize the original built-in delays. This could have been eliminated with a staggered starting procedure.

Cost Analysis

Based on the information previously given, the costs associated with the final simulation are: truck costs per minute = $0.50; batch-processing equipment cost per minute = $1.50; and paving machines–construction site crew costs per minute = $4.00. Assume also that the concrete is sold for $15.00 per cubic yard. Beginning with the line of Table 6.22 that reads 219.5 minutes, and ending with the line reading 1158.5 minutes, it is found that (1271.5 − 219.5) = 1052.0 minutes, which is the time required to deliver 560 cubic yards of concrete. In this period of time there were 56 trips with an average load of ten cubic yards, which account for the 56(10) = 560 cubic yards of concrete previously given. Thus the company will receive 560($15.00) = 8400 gross dollars for the portion of the contract. The combined cost, for the supplier, of $2.00 per minute, when multiplied by the total minutes, yields (1052.0 min)($2.00 cost/min) = $2104.00. This figure does not include all overhead and general-administrative costs; when these are added the profit for this simulation will decrease.

Additional cost information may also be informative:

Average Cost per Trip for One Truck

(Average min/trip)(Truck cost/min) = Average cost/trip for one truck

which yields:

(118.3 min/trip)($0.50/min) = $59.15 Average cost per trip for one truck

Average Waiting Time Cost per Truck

Truck waiting time before loading	1.7 min/truck
Truck waiting time before unloading	12.1 min/truck
Total	13.8 min/truck

Total truck waiting cost = (13.8 min)($0.50 Cost/min) = 6.90/truck

Average Batch-Processing Plant Waiting Time Cost per Truck

$$\text{Equipment waiting time} \quad = 9.1 \text{ min/truck}$$
$$\text{Cost for waiting @ } \$1.50/\text{min} = (9.1)(\$1.50) = \$13.65/\text{truck}$$

Average Construction Site Waiting Time Cost per Truck[16]

$$\text{Equipment waiting time} \quad = 1.5 \text{ min/truck}$$
$$\text{Cost for waiting @ } \$4.00 \text{ per min} = (1.5)(\$4.00) = \$6.00/\text{truck}$$

Conclusion of Cost Analysis

In a standard costing process, attention must be given to labor, burdens, materials, and general administrative costs. The information used thus far has included labor and burden costs because they were directly affected by queue size. Materials, however, are not affected except when the batch has to be discarded owing to age. General and administrative costs are similarly affected by waiting lines but cannot be calculated as easily as those associated with operational costs.

Using gross saving figures, a cost evaluation of this simulation (Table 6.22) can be made:[17]

Gross sales = [(Batches)(Selling price per batch)] − (sales lost due to rejected batches) = \$8400 − 0 = \$8400.00.

Operating costs = [(Minutes of operations)(Operating cost per min)]
                  + (penalty cost) = [(min of operation)(operating cost)]
                  + [(site waiting time cost per truck)(no. of trucks)]
                  = [(1052)(\$2.00)] + [(\$6.00)(56)] = (\$2104) + (\$336)
                  = \$2440.00.

Material costs = (Company's estimated cost per cubic yard) (Number of cubic yards furnished) = (\$5.00)(560) = \$2800.00.

---

[16] This figure was calculated to show the effects of waiting time on the construction-site phase of the operation. There is usually a penalty clause associated with the inability to deliver a specified amount of concrete; the supplying contractor cannot, then, discount the responsibilities here. In this problem it is assumed that the penalty equals the construction-site operating cost.

[17] Gross waiting-time costs are used in this analysis, but many accounting systems prefer that an analyst use only out-of-pocket costs when figuring savings. Usually, all direct labor savings are allowed as savings; but are all burden costs saved? For example, if waiting time were eliminated, the company would need a smaller total of trucks, less garage space, etc. Conversely, can all equipment be utilized—every minute? A company usually has excess capacity, and time savings may only increase idle time. This is argued by many authorities, with many recommending that only calculable savings be used in cost-justification studies. If this procedure were to be followed in this analysis, then savings would be: Direct labor + Out-of-pocket burden + Material + Zero general and administration—an exceptionally difficult and time-consuming method. Most authorities agree that time savings are worth while, especially when the savings come from methods-improvements that require a minimum of capital.

General and administrative costs = 10% of every sales dollar (company's estimate).

Thus   G & A = ($8400)(0.10) = $840.00

Gross profit = (Gross sales) − [(operating costs) + (material cost) + G & A costs)] = ($8400) − [($2440) + ($2800) + ($840)]
        = $2320.00.

Total cost
of waiting time = [(Average waiting time cost per truck) + (Average batch-processing plant waiting time per truck) + (Average construction site waiting cost per truck)] [(Number of trucks) (Number of trips per truck)] =

$$[(\$6.90) + (\$13.65) + (\$6.00)][(7)(8)] = \$1486.80$$

6.5 DISCUSSION AND REVIEW QUESTIONS

1. Example 1 involves random arrivals and constant service. Let us assume an opposite situation with arrivals every three and a half minutes and service times following the probability distribution of arrival times. Simulate three sets of fifteen samples, compare each set, and use the averages from the three sets to determine the average length of queue and the expected waiting time. See Sec. 6.41.

2. Simulate the emergency room problem as given in the case history of Appalachia Memorial Hospital. Find E_w, E_n, E_t, and E_Ψ. If you find that additional personnel are required, justify this by considering that a nurse costs the hospital in direct wages forty dollars per day and that each emergency call returns an average gross income of three dollars and fifty cents. Are costs really important in this situation? Are people going to leave the line? See Sec. 4.3.

3. Use the distributions given in Station 2 example 2, as the single line input (customers arriving per hour instead of pieces per minute) to a multichannel system with each station capable of servicing according to the distribution given in Station 1, example 2 (customers serviced per hour instead of pieces per minute) and determine the number of servicing stations required if servicing costs are five dollars per hour and waiting time costs (loss of customers due to excessive lines) are twenty-five cents per hour. See Sec. 6.42.

4. In a grocery supermarket the manager gives strict instructions to the check-out personnel to ring the bell for additional help whenever the line grows to ten customers, and *not to close it until the other line reaches two customers.* Given the following historically gathered information, what is your opinion of the manager's decision? What alternatives would you recommend?

Minutes Between Arrivals	Probability	Service Time (min)	Frequency
0.25	11	0.25	2
0.75	17	0.75	8
1.25	24	1.25	13
1.75	27	1.75	24
2.25	10	2.25	16
2.75	6	2.75	9
3.25	3	3.25	3
3.75	1		——
4.25	1		75

Consider that when the bell rings, personnel come from another area—departing their present duties to assist in the check-out operations. This results in additional check-out costs plus the lost work in the area from which they come. Assume that a check-out clerk earns one hundred dollars per week and that the relief help earns one hundred and twenty-five dollars.

To assist you in this problem, we shall take up this simulation at trial 30, when there are seven waiting for service. Customer 36 is finished at 65.50 minutes. At that time there are nine others waiting. Customer 45 enters at 65.00 min but still must wait for customer 36 to conclude service.

Number	Arrival Time	Waiting Time	Service Begins	Service Time	Service Ends	Queue Length
30	44.25	7.50	51.75	2.75	54.50	7
31	46.50	8.00	54.50	2.25	56.75	7
32	48.25	8.50	56.75	2.25	59.00	7
33	49.50	9.50	59.00	2.25	61.25	9
34	50.75	10.50	61.25	0.75	62.00	9
35	52.00	10.00	62.00	1.75	63.75	8
36	53.75	10.00	63.75	1.75	65.50	9
37	54.50	11.00	65.50	2.25	67.75	9
38	56.25	11.50	67.75	1.75	69.50	10 bell rings)
39	58.00	11.50	69.50	1.75	71.25	10
40	59.25	12.00	71.25	1.25	72.50	10 (help arrives)
41	60.00	12.50	72.50	2.25	74.75	5 (line splits)
42	60.25					
43	61.50					
44	64.25					
45	65.00					
46	66.25					
47	68.00					
48	69.25					
49	70.50					
50	71.75					
51	74.00					

Assume that two additional customers enter the system before the alternate line opens; also, that the line will split equally and that arriving customers go to the shortest line. (When studying lines in a supermarket, you will find that the line usually divides unequally.)

When considering alternatives to this problem, be sure to consider other tolerances for the line. For example, ring the bell for help upon line's growing to eight customers, and do not leave until there is only one in the original check-out station; also, tie in the economy associated with the operation.

5. Some marketing studies show that newly-arriving customers will buy less if they see large waiting lines at the check-out counter. Assume that lost purchases develop geometrically where $a = 0.0002$ and $r = 2$. Lost sales for ten in the line equals $1 = ar^{n-1} = (0.0002)(2)^9 = \$0.1024$. Carrying this to extremes, one could envision that customer losses would soon be greater than gains; but do not potential customers sometimes turn from a store when lines are excessive?

Using these data and concepts, what solution would you give to Problem 4?

6. Rework Example 3 with three clerks to determine whether this is a more economical operation. See Sec. 6.43.

7. Solve the obstetrical case of Chap. 4 from Appalachia Memorial Hospital using simulation techniques. See Sec. 4.5.

8. Solve Example 1 from Chapter 5 using simulation techniques. See Sec. 5.11.

9. Assume that emergency patients have the following hypothetical priority distributions:

Daily Priorities		Probability	Service Length (min)	Probability
0	0	0.002	10	001
1	1440	0.010	20	001
2	720	0.043	30	005
3	480	0.117	40	020
4	360	0.205	50	071
5	285	0.246	60	147
6	240	0.205	70	220
7	206	0.117	80	236
8	180	0.043	90	177
9	160	0.010	100	089
10	144	0.002	110	026
11	131		120	007

How would you assimilate this into the data already gathered if priorities caused all others to wait? One method frequently used is to tie this distribution to the arrival distribution (Sec. 2.3).

10. To better understand the power of simulation, rework Example 2 through sets of twenty-five simulations, but this time you are allowed to change the machine's feed rate and the number of personnel at channels two and three.

Recommend the most economical procedure, i.e., more personnel at various stations, additional or fewer machines, etc. Consider the following cost data:[18]

1. Lehr stopped	$300/hr
2. One machine cost (includes operator)	$50/hr
3. Space cost (additional lehr belt)	$150/ft
4. One personnel cost (station 1)	$10/hr
(station 2)	$7/hr
5. Relief help (any station)	$15/hr
6. Cost of taking products off line and then replacing	$30/hr

7. Starting space between each station equals: 1–2 = 200 tubes; 2–3 = 150 tubes; 3 to end of lehr = 300 tubes
8. Cost to move station 1, $3000; station 2, $100; station 3, $400
9. Inventory area: station 1–2, $100/100 tubes
                        station 2–3, $50/100 tubes

To simplify the problem consider that these are the only products to contend with and that the line is used exclusively by these three stations.

11. Work Example 4, Section 6.44, when the trip has been increased to 11.25 miles with an average time of forty-five minutes. Does the same number of trucks constitute the most economical system?

12. The average speed in Example 4, Section 6.44, is 25 mph. Every value of Table 6.15 was increased by 1.5, which resulted in Table 6.16. The average speed of Table 6.16 is also 25 mph. Why is the average speed in Table 6.15 different from the average speed in Table 6.16, when the time of each is decreased by two minutes? For example, $7.5/28 = 0.268$, while $11.25/43 = 0.262$.

13. Work Example 4, Sec. 6.44, when the batch is rejected for concrete more than eighty minutes old. Remember that this truck will require the same dumping time but that it will leave the construction site available for immediate use—otherwise waiting time will increase.

14. Is Example 4, Sec. 6.44, find the most economical assignment of trucks to the system?

---

[18] Not all data may be relevant to the problem.

Tableau 6.23

06268	11860	83699	38631	90045	69696	48572	05917	51905	10052
03550	59144	59468	37984	77892	89766	86489	46619	50263	91136
22188	81205	99699	84260	19693	36701	43233	62719	53117	71153
63759	61429	14043	49095	84746	22018	19014	76781	61086	90216
55006	17765	15013	77707	54317	48862	53823	52905	70754	68212
81972	45644	12600	01951	72166	52682	97598	11955	73018	23528
06344	50136	33122	31794	86423	58037	36065	32190	31367	96007
92363	99784	94169	03652	80824	33407	40837	97749	18364	72666
96083	16943	89916	55159	62184	86208	09764	20244	88388	98675
92993	10747	08985	44999	36785	65035	65933	77378	92339	96454
95083	70292	50394	61044	65591	09774	16216	63561	59751	78771
77308	60721	96057	86031	83148	34970	30892	53489	44999	18021
11913	49624	28510	27311	61586	28576	43092	69971	44220	80410
70648	47484	05095	92335	55299	27161	64486	71307	85883	69610
92771	99203	37786	81142	44271	36433	31726	74879	89348	76886
78816	20975	13043	55921	82774	62745	48338	88348	61211	88074
79934	35392	56097	87613	94627	63622	08110	16611	88599	02890
64698	83376	87524	36897	17215	74339	69856	43622	22567	11518
44212	12995	03581	37618	94851	63020	65348	55857	91742	79508
82292	00204	00579	70630	37136	50922	83387	15014	51838	81760
08692	87237	87879	01629	72184	33853	95144	67943	19345	03469
67927	76855	50702	78555	97442	78809	40575	79714	06201	34576
62167	94213	52971	85974	68067	78814	40103	70759	92129	46716
45828	45441	74220	84157	23241	49332	23646	09390	13032	51569
01164	35307	26526	80335	58090	85871	07205	31749	40571	51755
29283	31581	04359	45538	41435	61103	32428	94042	39971	63678
19868	49978	81699	84904	50163	22625	07845	71308	00859	87984
14294	93587	55960	23149	07370	65065	06580	46285	07884	83928
77410	52195	29459	23032	83242	89938	40510	27252	55565	64714
36580	06921	35675	81645	60479	71035	99380	59759	42161	93440
07780	18093	31258	78156	07871	20369	53947	08534	39433	57216
07548	08454	36674	46255	80541	42903	37366	21164	97516	66181
22023	60448	69344	44260	90570	01632	21002	24413	04671	05665
20827	37210	57797	34660	32510	71558	78228	42304	77197	79168
47802	79270	48805	59480	88092	11441	96016	76091	51823	94442
76730	86591	18978	25479	77684	88439	35112	26052	57112	91653
26439	02903	20935	76297	15290	84688	74002	09467	41111	19194
32927	83426	07848	59327	44422	53372	27823	25417	27150	21750
51484	05286	77103	47284	05578	88774	15293	50740	07932	87633
45142	96804	92834	26886	70002	96643	36008	02239	93563	66429
12760	96106	89348	76127	17058	37181	74001	43869	28377	80923
15564	38648	02147	03894	97787	35234	44302	41672	12408	90168
71051	34941	55384	70709	11646	30269	60154	28276	48153	23122
42742	08817	82579	19505	26344	94116	86230	49139	32644	36545
59474	97752	77124	79579	65448	87700	54002	81411	57988	57437
12581	18211	61713	73962	87212	55624	85675	33961	63272	17587
00278	75089	20673	37438	92361	47941	62056	94104	45502	79159
59317	31861	62559	32055	23055	70922	47195	29827	68065	95409
59220	42448	70881	33687	53575	54599	69525	76424	98778	10459
00670	32157	15877	87120	13857	23979	38922	62421	03043	19602

○ = Circled Numbers = Starting point for each trial of ten numbers given in Sec. 6.21, Example 1.

[19] David W. Miller and Martin K. Starr, *Executive Decisions and Operations Research* (Prentice-Hall, Inc., Englewood Cliffs, N. J., 1960, p. 356).

Bibliography

Bierman, Harold, Jr., Charles F. Bonini, Lawrence E. Fouraker, Robert K. Jaedicke, *Quantitative Analysis for Business Decisions*. Homewood, Ill.: Richard D. Irwin, Inc., 1965.

Bowman, Edward H., Robert B. Fetter, *Analysis for Production Management*. Homewood, Ill.: Richard D. Irwin, Inc., 1961.

————, ————, *Analyses of Industrial Operations*. Homewood, Ill.: Richard D. Irwin, Inc., 1959.

Churchman, C. West, Russel L. Ackoff, E. Leonard Arnoff, *Introduction to Operations Research*. New York: John Wiley & Sons, Inc., 1963.

diRoccaferrera, Giuseppe M. Ferrero, *Operations Research Models for Business and Industry*. Cincinnati, Ohio: South-Western Publishing Company, 1964.

Feller, William, *An Introduction to Probability Theory and Its Applications*. New York: John Wiley & Sons, Inc., 1965.

Horowitz, Ira, *An Introduction to Quantitative Business Analysis*. New York: McGraw-Hill Book Company, 1965.

Kemeny, John G., Arthur Schleifer Jr., J. Laurie Snell, Gerald L. Thompson, *Finite Mathematics with Business Applications*. Englewood Cliffs, N. J.: Prentice-Hall, Inc., 1964.

Maynard, H. B., *Industrial Engineering Handbook*. New York: McGraw-Hill Book Company, 1965.

Miller, David W., Martin K. Starr, *Executive Decisions and Operations Research*. Englewood Cliffs, N. J.: Prentice-Hall, Inc., 1964.

Niebel, Benjamin W., *Motion and Time Study*. Homewood, Ill.: Richard D. Irwin, Inc., 1962.

Parzen, Emanuel, *Stochastic Processes*. San Francisco: Holden-Day, Inc., 1962.

Sasieni, Maurice, Arthur Yaspen, Lawrence Friedman, *Operations Research Methods and Problems*. New York: John Wiley & Sons, Inc., 1959.

Schaifer, Robert, *Probability and Statistics for Business Decisions*. New York: McGraw-Hill Book Company, 1959.

Index